Non-verbal Reasoning

Rapid Tests 2

Rebecca Brant

Schofield&Sims

Introduction

This book gives you practice in answering non-verbal reasoning questions quickly.

The questions are like the questions on the 11+ and other school selection tests. You must find the correct answers.

School selection tests are usually timed, so you need to get used to working quickly. Each test has a target time for you to work towards. You should time how long you spend on each test, or you can ask an adult to time you.

All the questions in this book are multiple choice. For each question you are given a choice of answers. Choose the answer you think is correct and draw a circle round the letter beneath it.

What you need

- A pencil
- An eraser
- A clock, watch or stopwatch
- A sheet of rough paper
- An adult to help you work out how long you take and to mark the test for you

What to do

- Turn to **Section 1 Test 1** on page 4. Look at the grey box at the top of the page labelled **Target time**. This tells you how long the test should take.
- When you are ready to start, write down the time or start the stopwatch. Or the adult helping you will tell you when to begin.
- Find this black arrow ↓ near the top of the first page. Start each test here.
- Find this square ■. The instructions for the first set of questions are beside it. Read them carefully.
- Look below the instructions. Read the **Example**. Work out why the answer given is correct.
- Using similar methods, answer each question.
- Try to answer every question. If you do get stuck on a question, leave it and go on to the next one. Work quickly and try your best.
- When you have finished the first page, go straight onto the next page without waiting. Here you may find a different question type. Again, read the instructions and the example. Then answer the questions.
- When you reach the end, stop. Write down the time or stop the stopwatch. Or tell the adult that you have finished.
- With the adult, work out how long you took to do the test. Fill in the **Time taken** box at the end of the test.
- The adult will mark your test and fill in the **Score** and **Target met?** boxes.
- Turn to the **Progress chart** on page 40. Write your score in the box and colour in the graph to show how many questions you got right.
- Did you get some questions wrong? You should always have another go at them before you look at the answers. Then ask the adult to check your work and help you if you are still not sure.
- Later, you will do some more of these tests. You will soon learn to work through them more quickly. The adult who is helping you will tell you what to do next.

Published by **Schofield & Sims Ltd,**
7 Mariner Court, Wakefield, West Yorkshire, WF4 3FL, UK
Telephone 01484 607080
www.schofieldandsims.co.uk

First published in 2014

Second impression 2019

Author: ***Rebecca Brant****. Rebecca Brant has asserted her moral right under the Copyright, Designs and Patents Act, 1988, to be identified as the author of this work.*

British Library Cataloguing in Publication Data. *A catalogue record for this book is available from the British Library.*

Commissioned by ***Carolyn Richardson Publishing Services*** *(www.publiserve.co.uk)*

Design by ***Oxford Designers & Illustrators***
Front cover design by ***Ledgard Jepson Ltd***
Printed in the UK by ***Page Bros (Norwich) Ltd***
ISBN 978 07217 1464 6

Contents

A **pull-out answers section** (pages A1 to A8) appears in the centre of this book, between pages 20 and 21. It also gives simple guidance on how best to use this book. Remove this section before the child begins working through the tests.

Target time: **6 minutes**

Which picture on the right belongs to the group on the left? Circle the letter.

Example

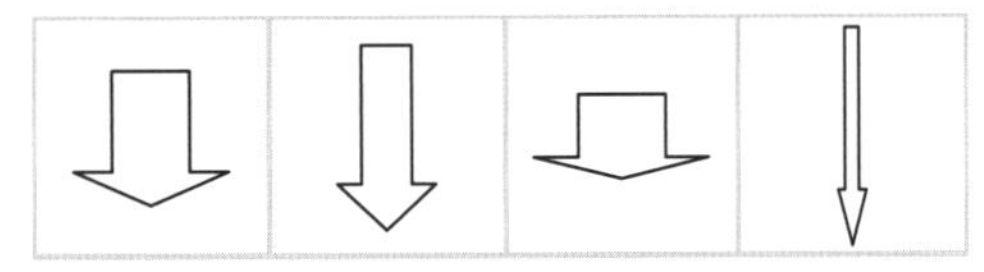

 a  b 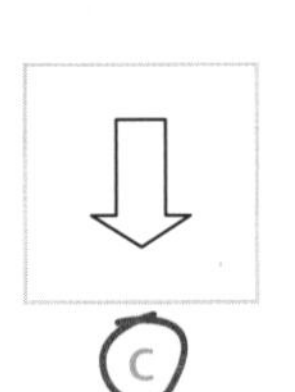 c 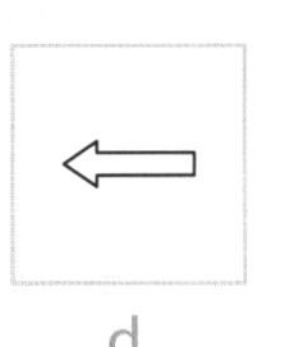 d 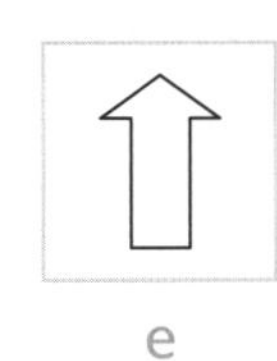 e

1.

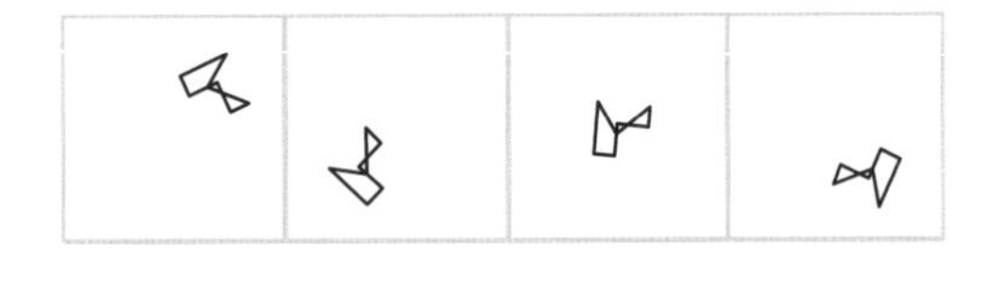

 a 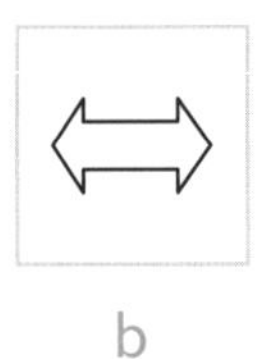 b  c 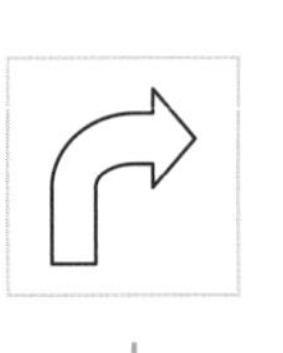 d 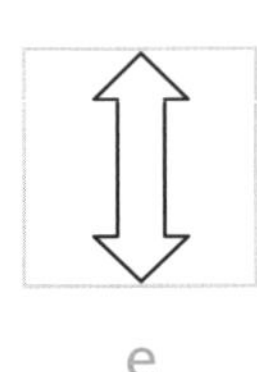 e

2.

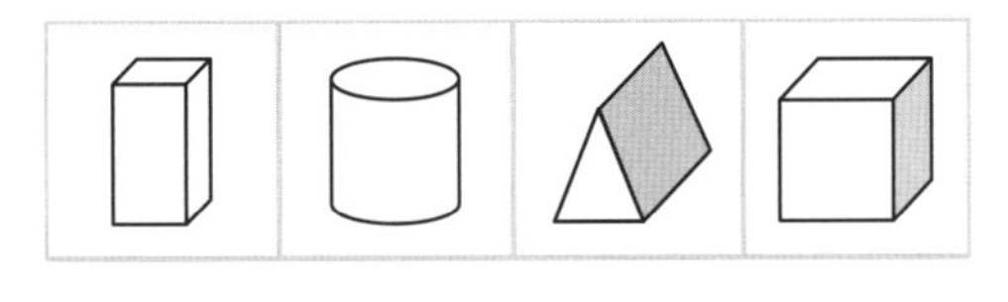

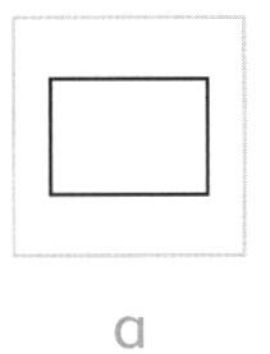 a 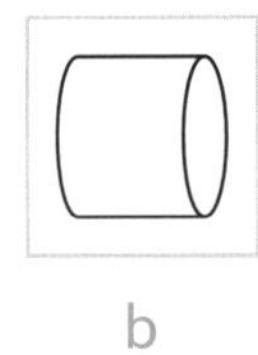 b  c 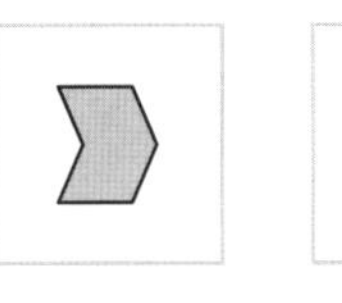 d e

3.

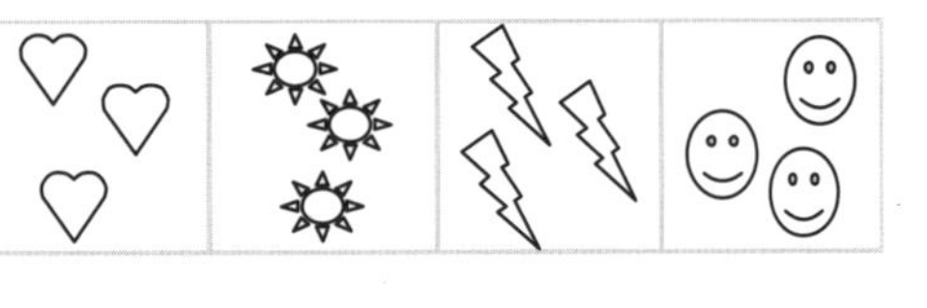

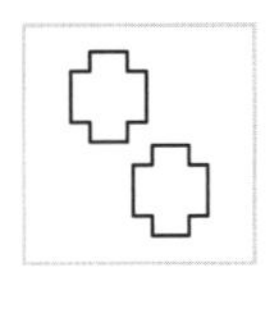 a 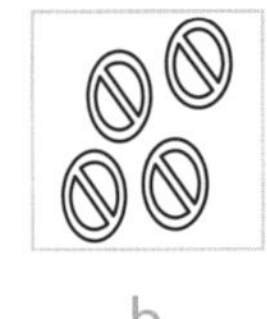 b 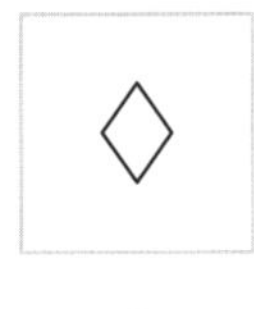 c  d  e

4.

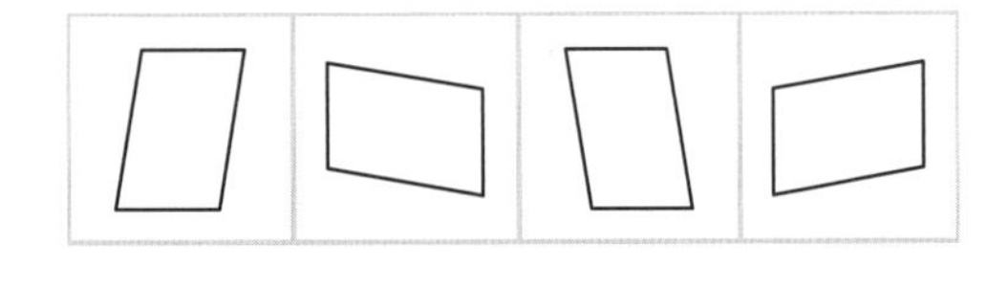

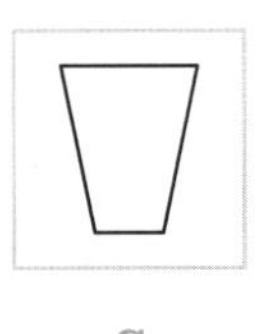 a 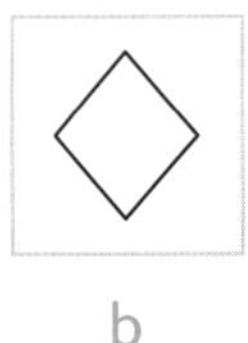 b 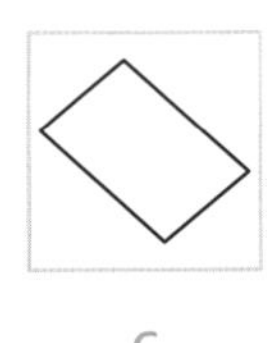 c 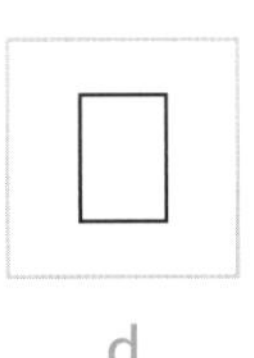 d 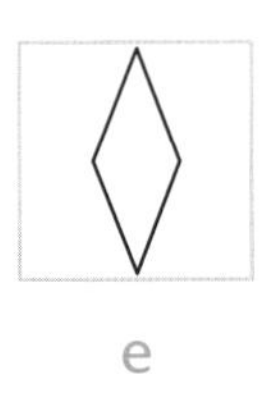 e

5.

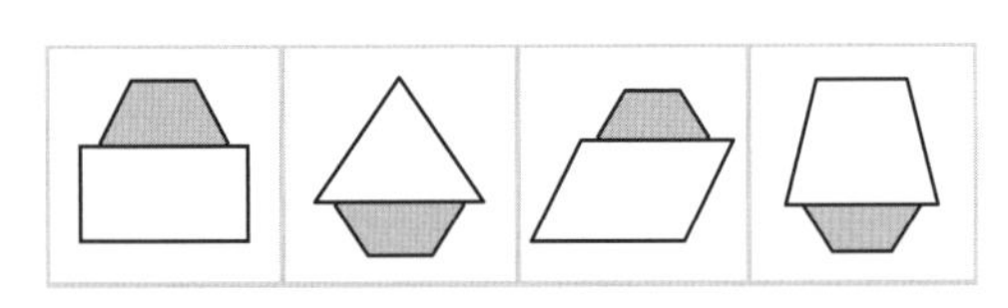

 a 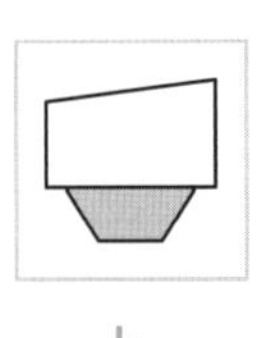 b 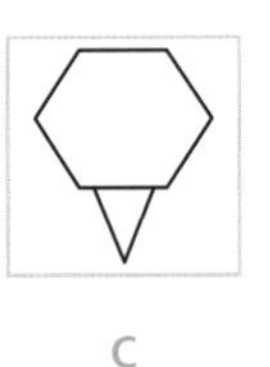 c 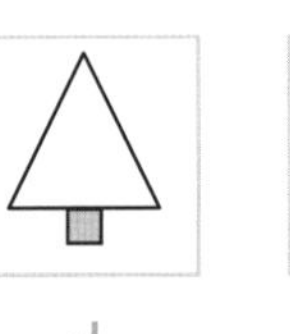 d 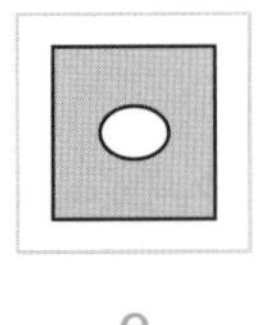 e

6.

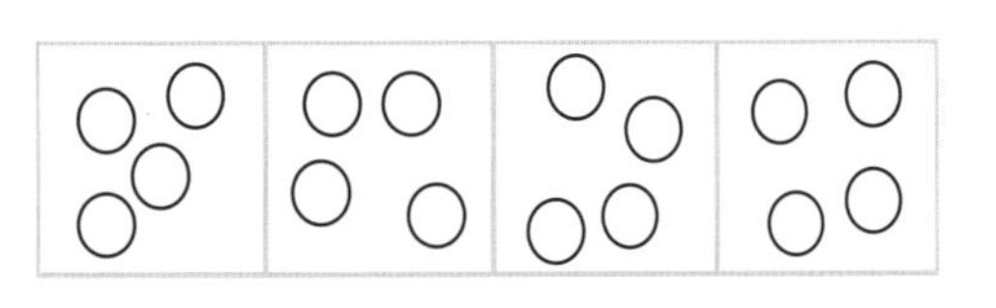

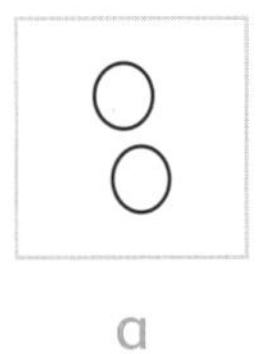 a 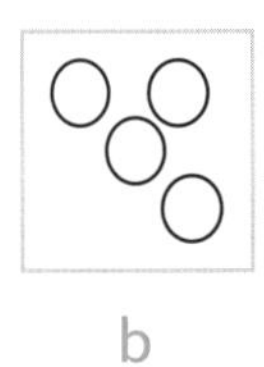 b 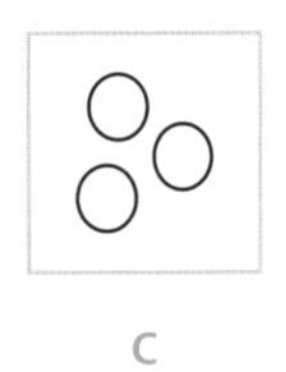 c 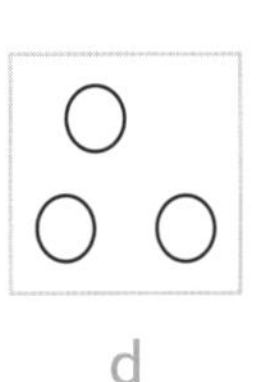 d 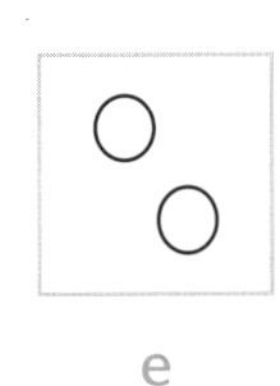 e

Now go on to the next page ➔

Which picture is the odd one out? Circle the letter.

Example

				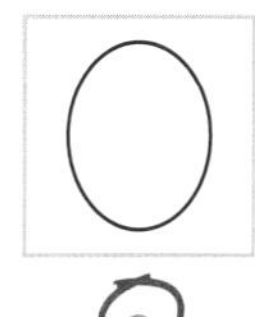
a	b	c	d	e

7.

	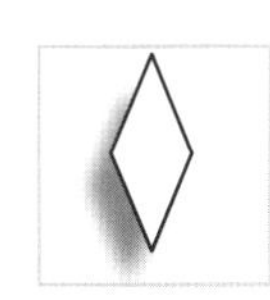	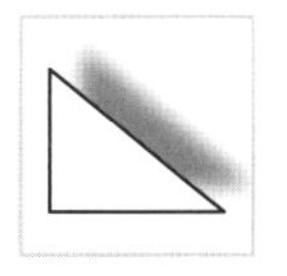	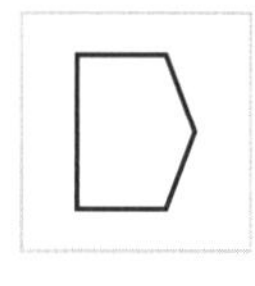	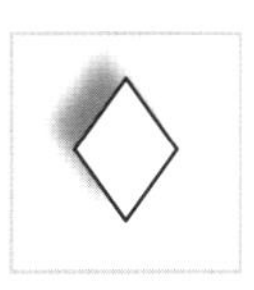
a	b	c	d	e

8.

			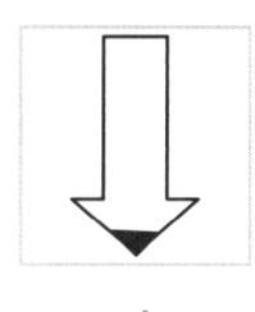	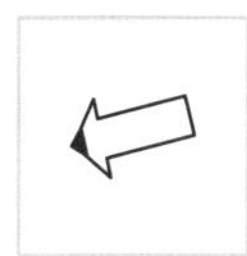
a	b	c	d	e

9.

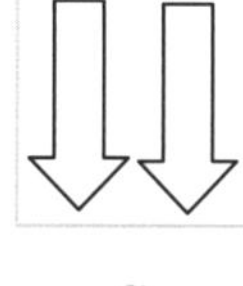	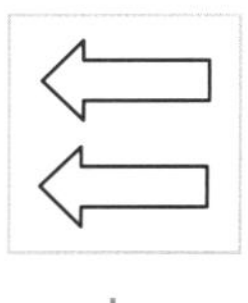			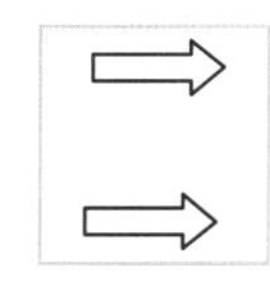
a	b	c	d	e

10.

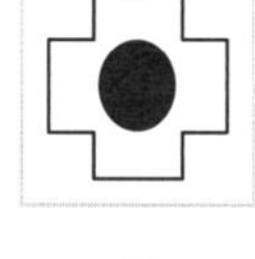	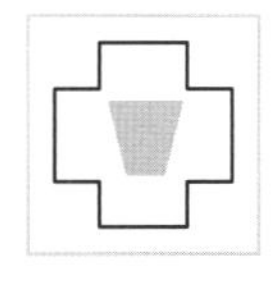	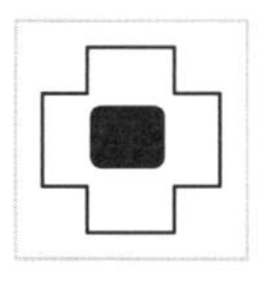	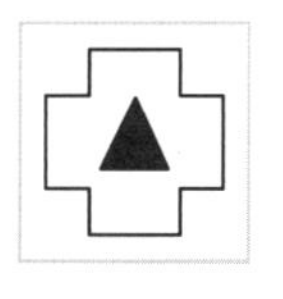	
a	b	c	d	e

11.

			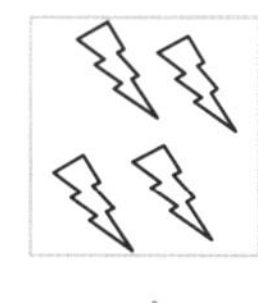	
a	b	c	d	e

12.

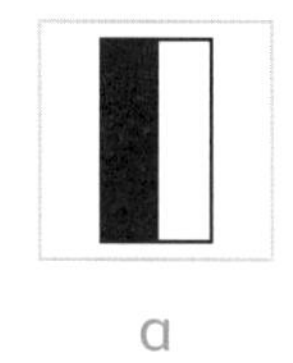		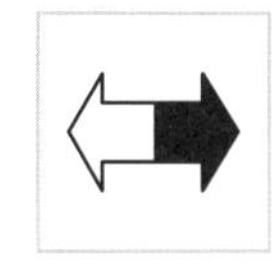		
a	b	c	d	e

End of test

Score:		**Time taken:**		**Target met?**	

Target time: **6 minutes**

The first two pictures go together. Which of the five pictures on the right goes with the third picture in the same way? Circle the letter.

Example

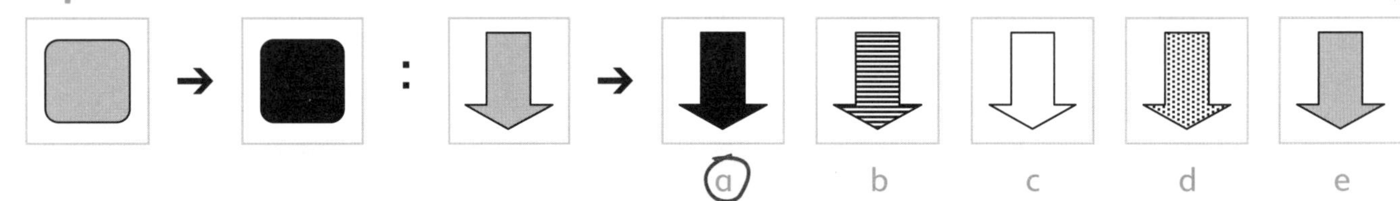

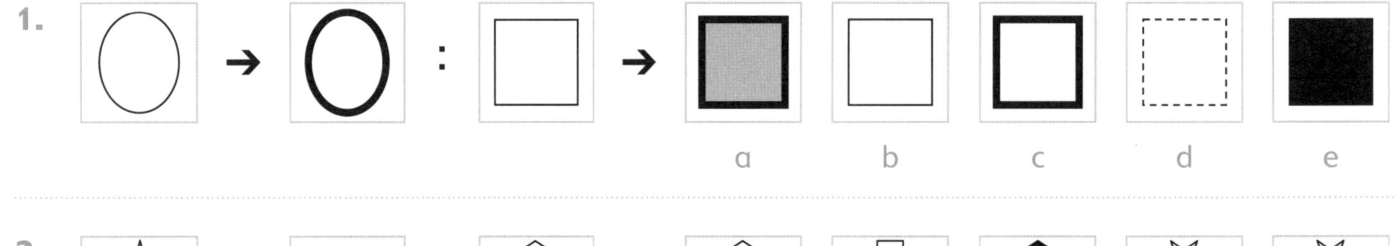

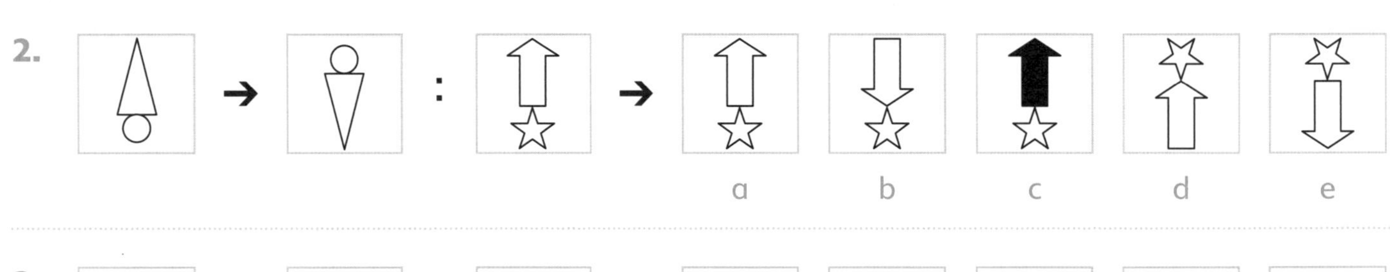

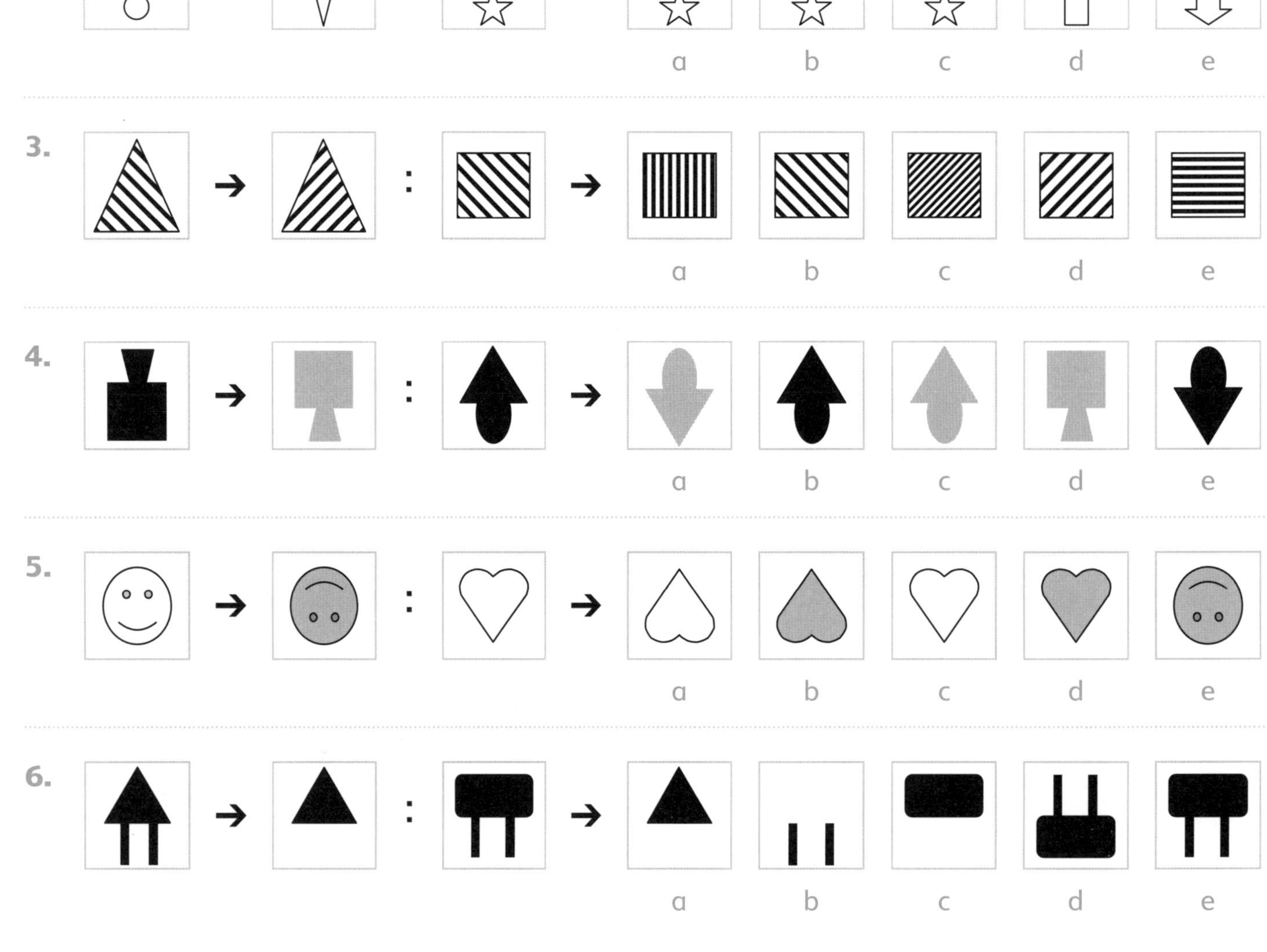

Now go on to the next page ➔

Which picture on the right goes in the empty space? Circle the letter.

Example

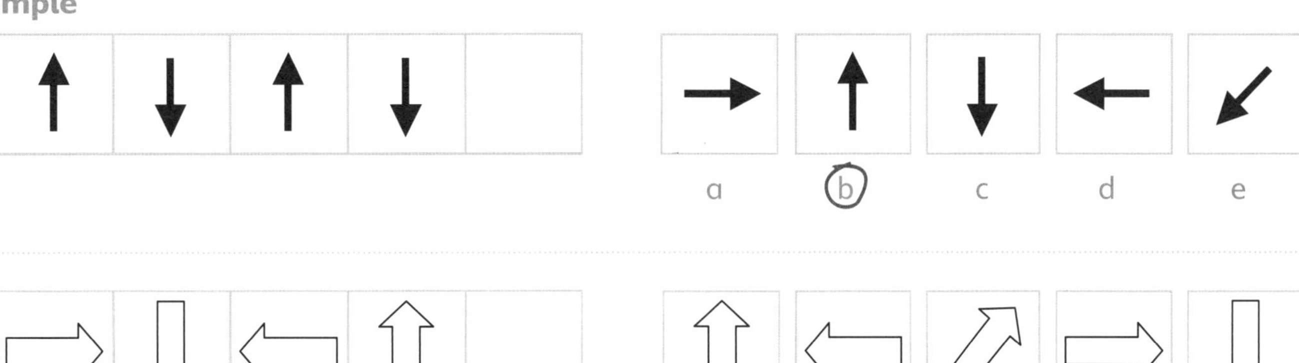

7.

8.

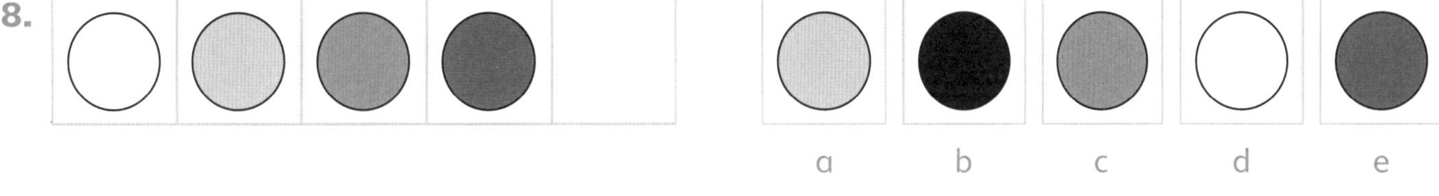

9.

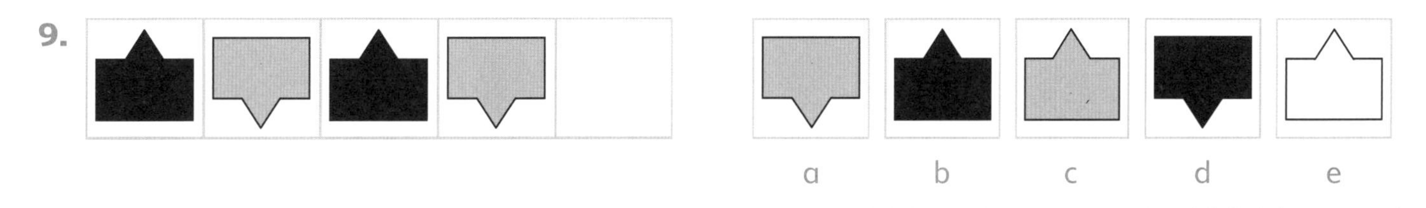

10.

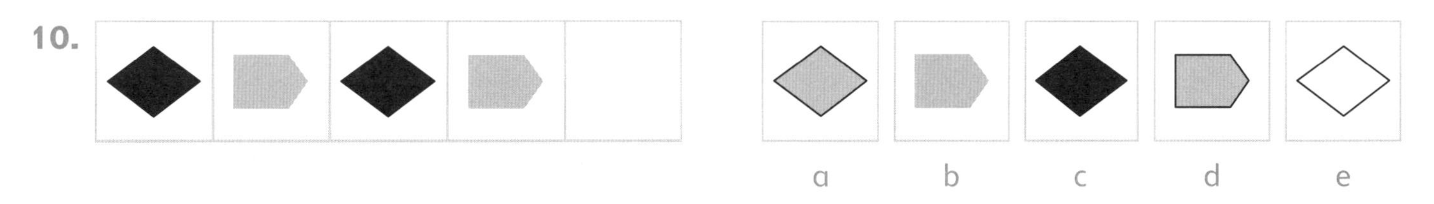

11.

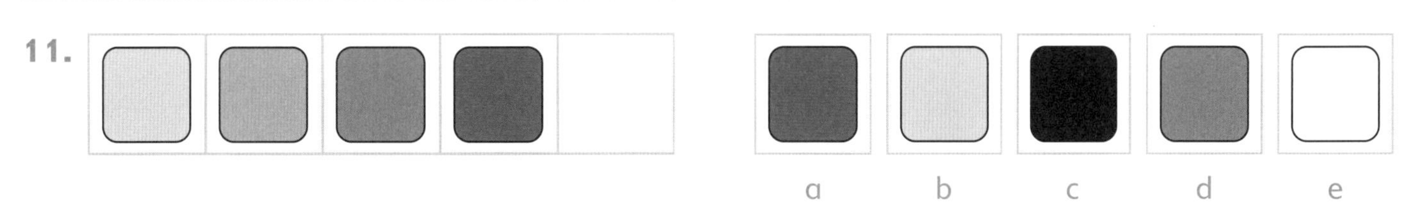

12.

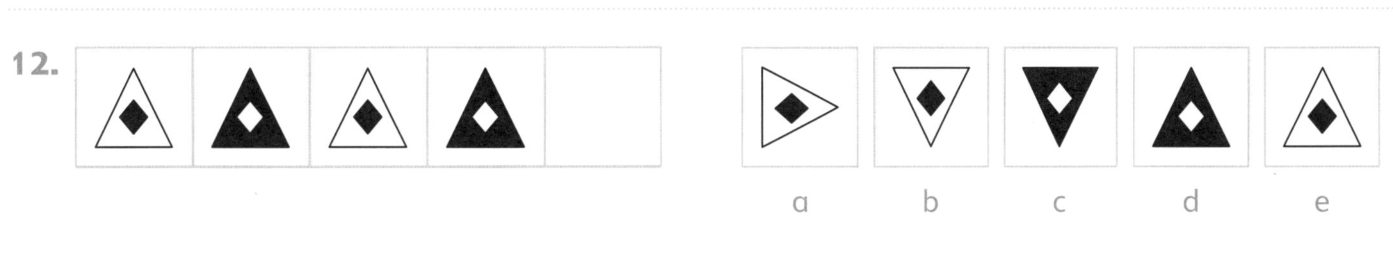

End of test

Score:		Time taken:		Target met?	

Target time: **6 minutes**

In which picture on the right is the picture on the left hidden? Circle the letter.

Example

					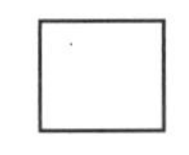	
		a	b	c	d	e
1.	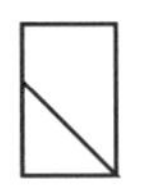		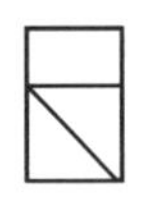			
		a	b	c	d	e
2.	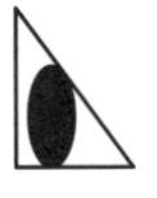				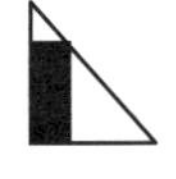	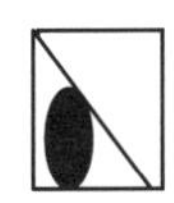
		a	b	c	d	e
3.		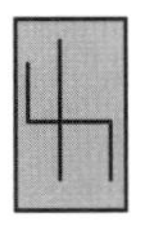	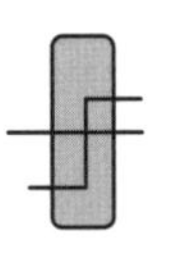		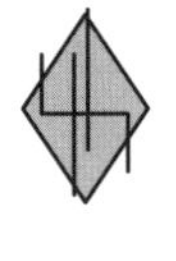	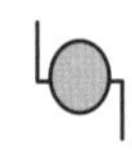
		a	b	c	d	e
4.						
		a	b	c	d	e
5.						
		a	b	c	d	e
6.						
		a	b	c	d	e

Now go on to the next page ➔

Pretend the dotted line is a mirror. Which picture on the right is a reflection of the picture on the left? Circle the letter.

Example

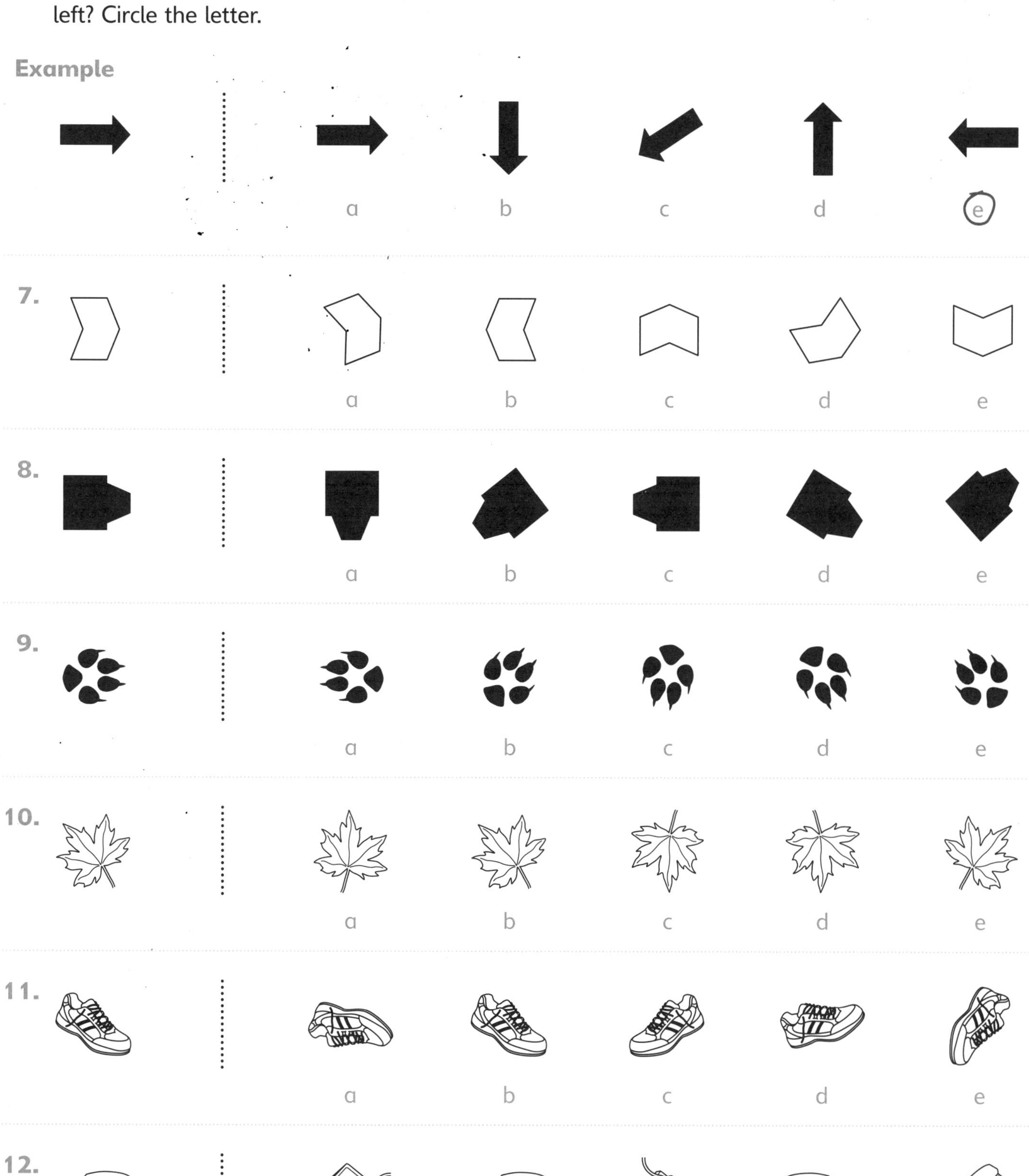

End of test

Score: | **Time taken:** | **Target met?**

Target time: **6 minutes**

Which of the pictures on the right best fits into the space in the grid? Circle the letter.

Example

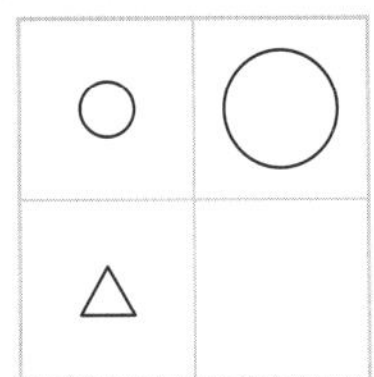

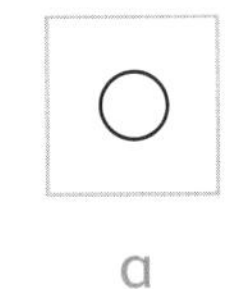 a

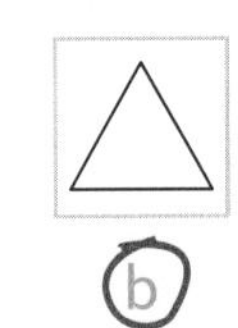 b

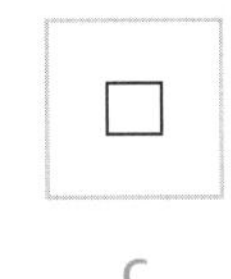 c

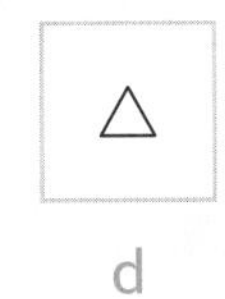 d

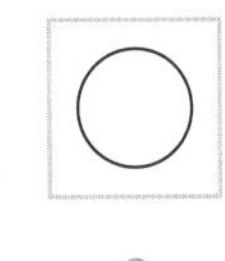 e

1.

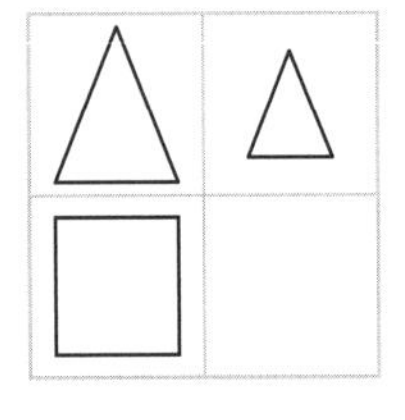

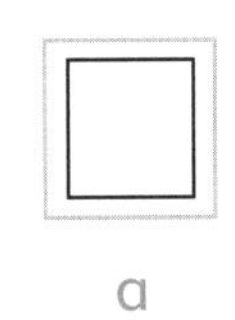 a

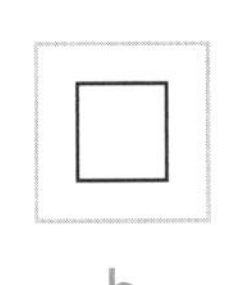 b

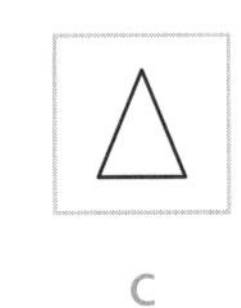 c

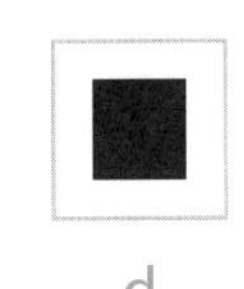 d

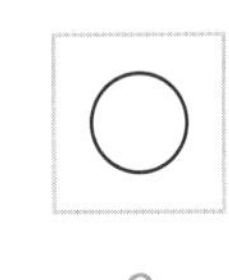 e

2.

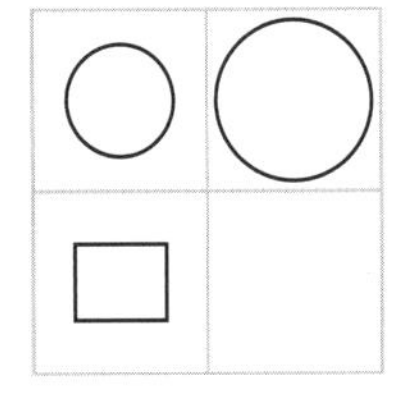

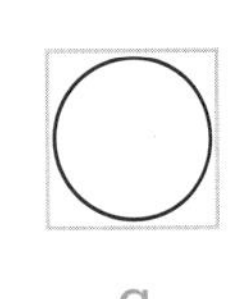 a

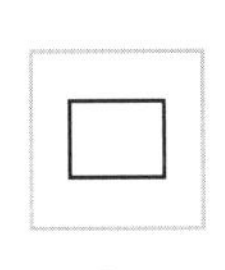 b

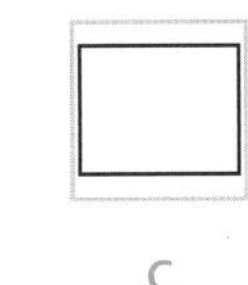 c

 d

 e

3.

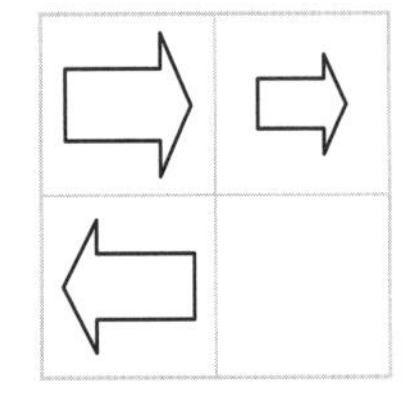

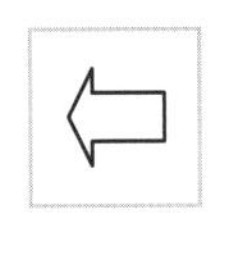 a

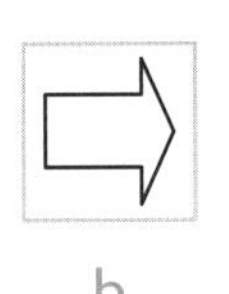 b

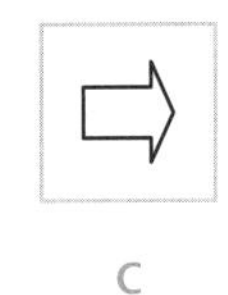 c

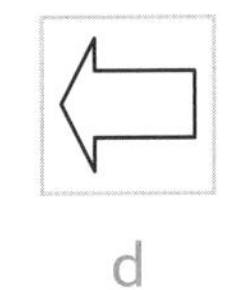 d

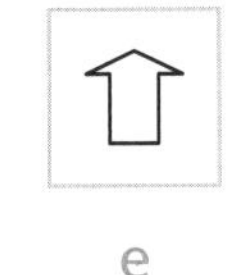 e

4.

 a

 b

 c

 d

 e

5.

 a

 b

 c

 d

 e

Now go on to the next page ➔

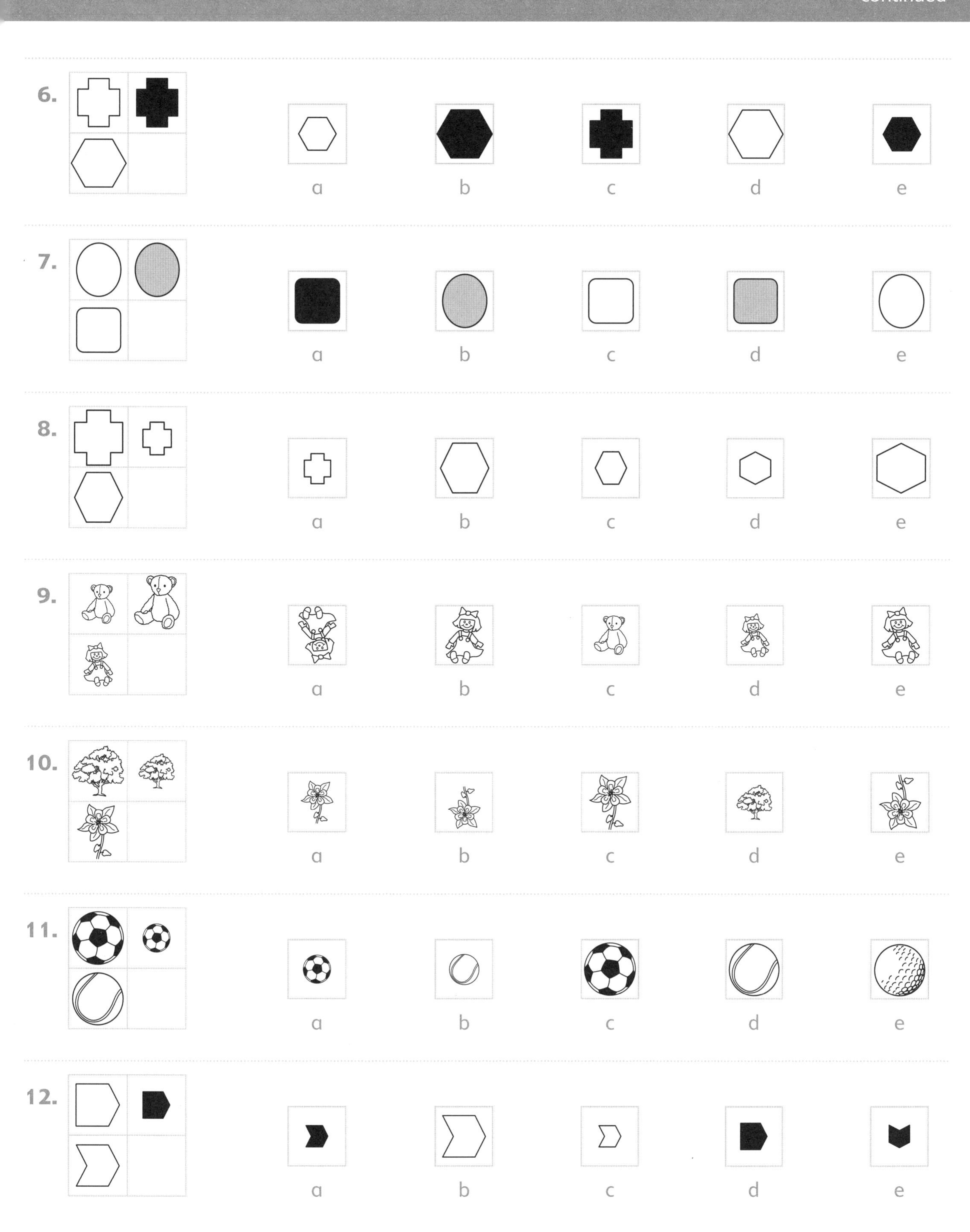

End of test

Score:		Time taken:		Target met?	

Target time: **6 minutes**

Which picture on the right goes in the empty space? Circle the letter.

Example

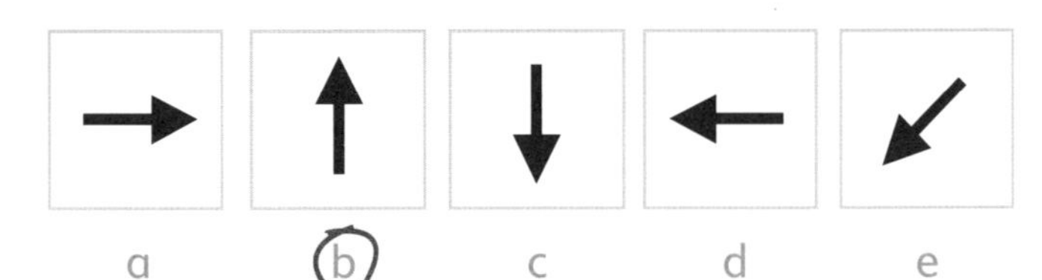

a (b) c d e

1.

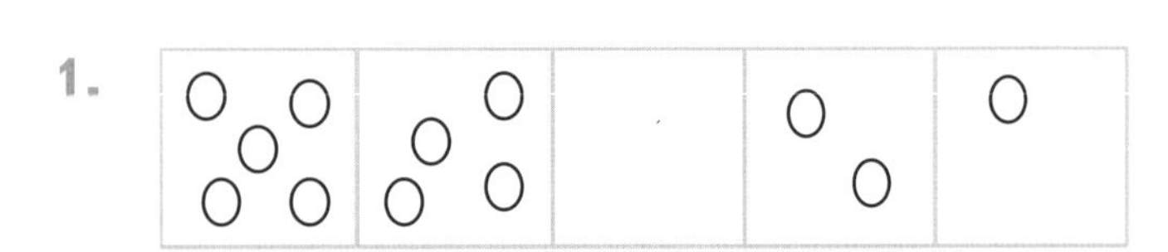

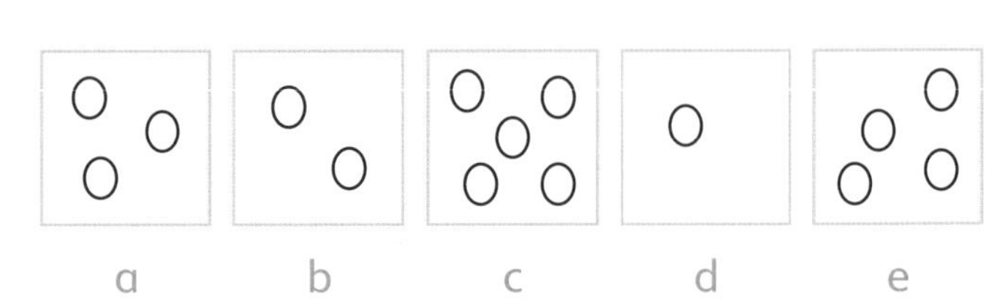

a b c d e

2.

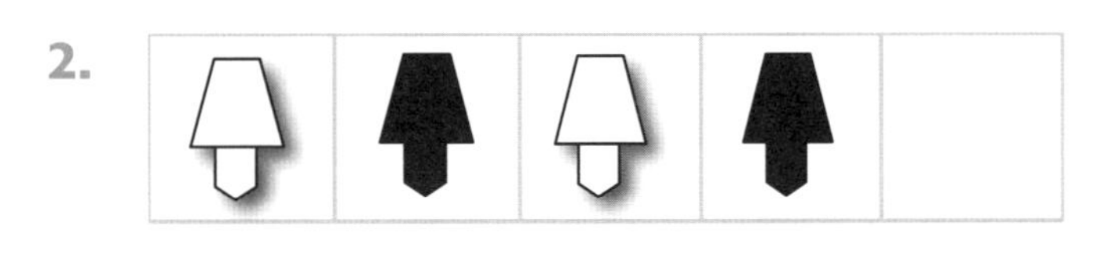

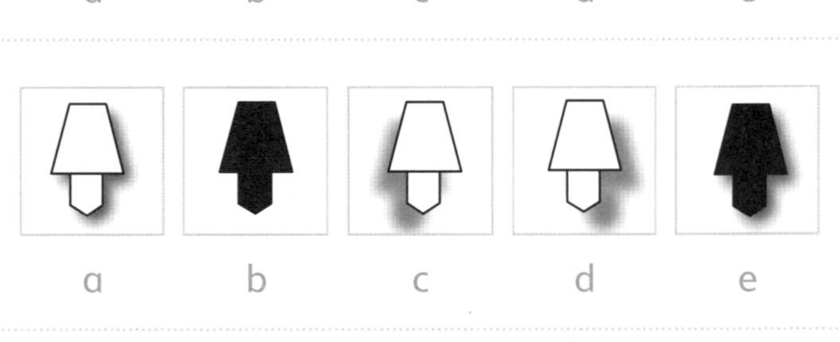

a b c d e

3.

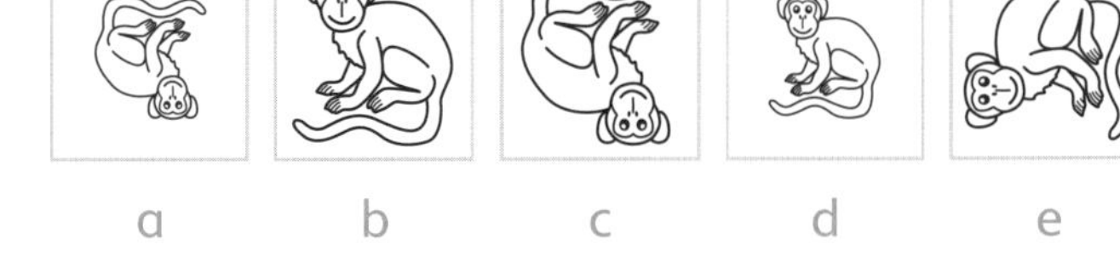

a b c d e

4.

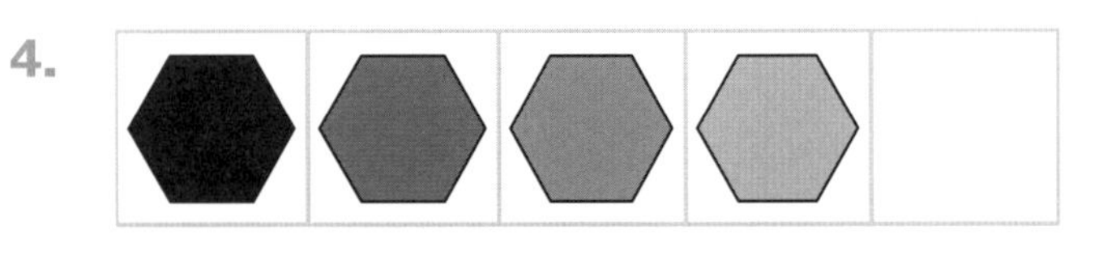

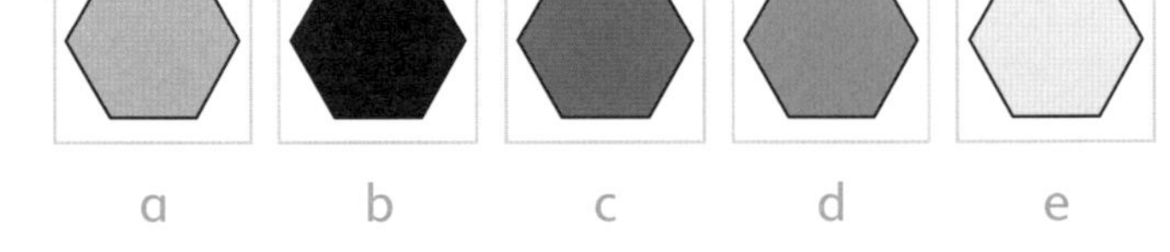

a b c d e

5.

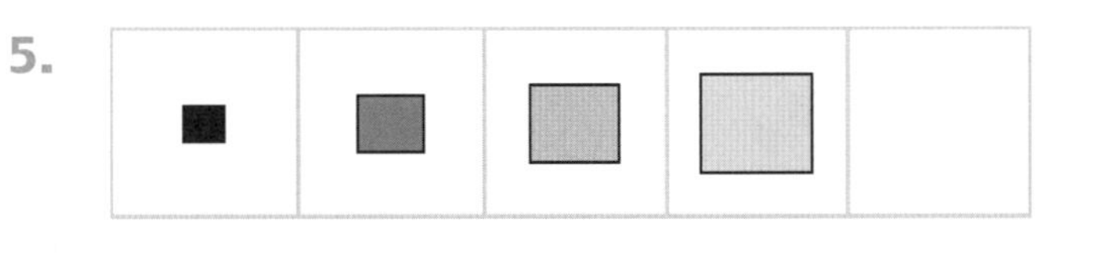

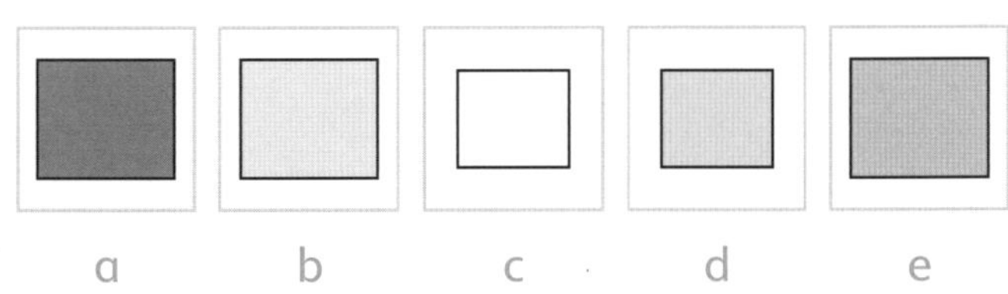

a b c d e

6.

a b c d e

Now go on to the next page ➔

In which picture on the right is the picture on the left hidden? Circle the letter.

Example

   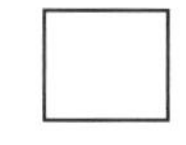 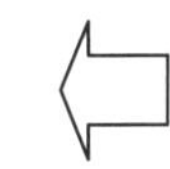

a b c d e

7. 

a b c d e

8. 

  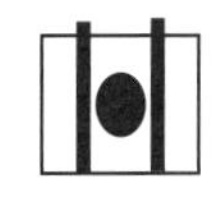  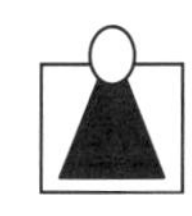

a b c d e

9. 

a b c d e

10. 

  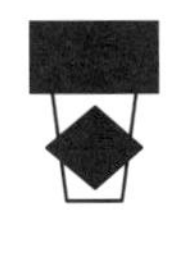  

a b c d e

11. 

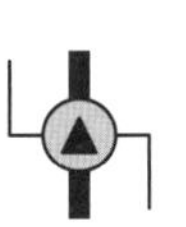  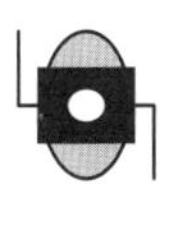  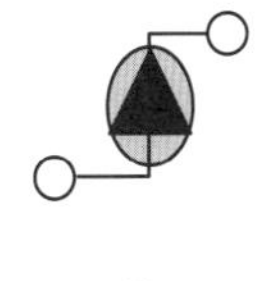

a b c d e

12. 

a b c d e

End of test

Score:		Time taken:		Target met?	

Target time: **6 minutes**

Pretend the dotted line is a mirror. Which picture on the right is a reflection of the picture on the left? Circle the letter.

Example

    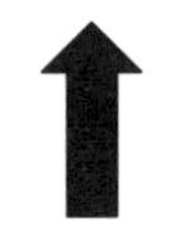 

a b c d (e)

1.     

a b c d e

2.     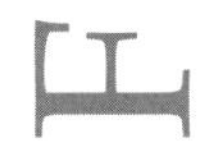 

a b c d e

3.    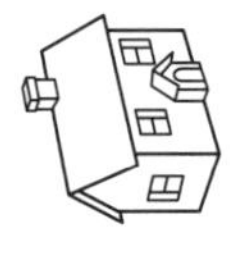  

a b c d e

4.      

a b c d e

5.      

a b c d e

6.      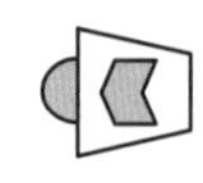

a b c d e

Now go on to the next page ➔

Which of the pictures on the right best fits into the space in the grid? Circle the letter.

Example

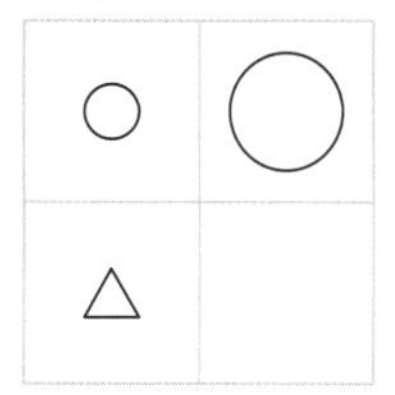

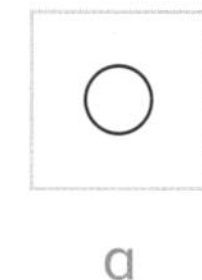
a

b

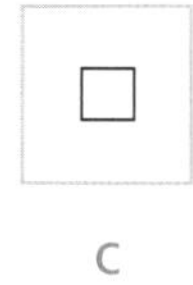
c

d

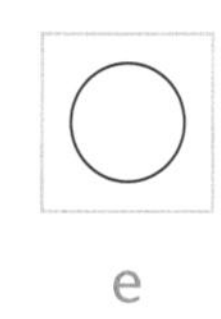
e

7.

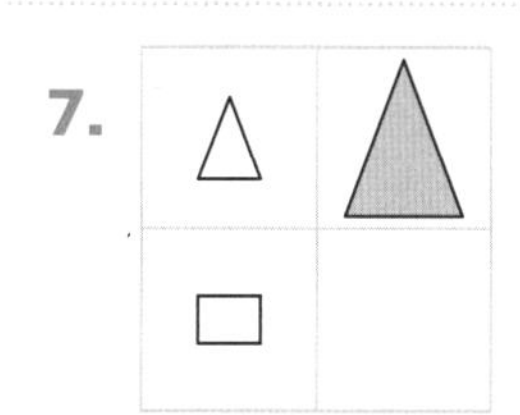

a

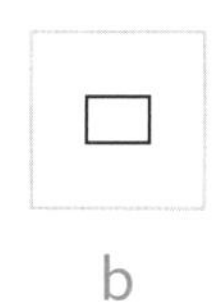
b

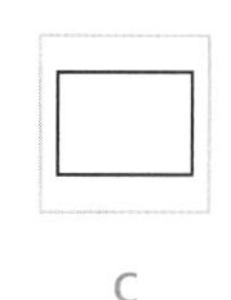
c

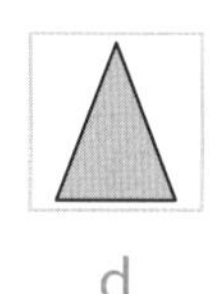
d

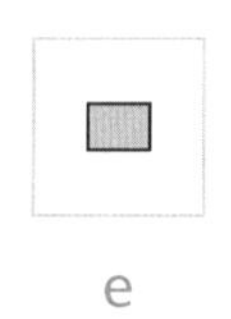
e

8.

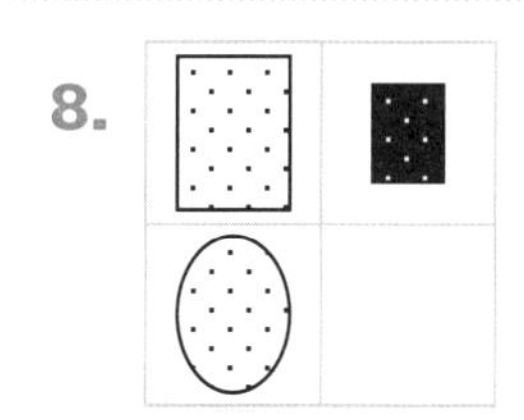

a

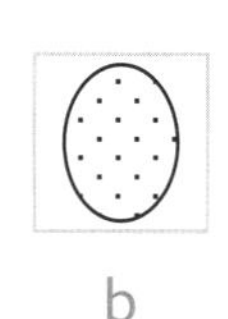
b

c

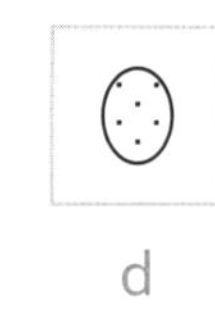
d

e

9.

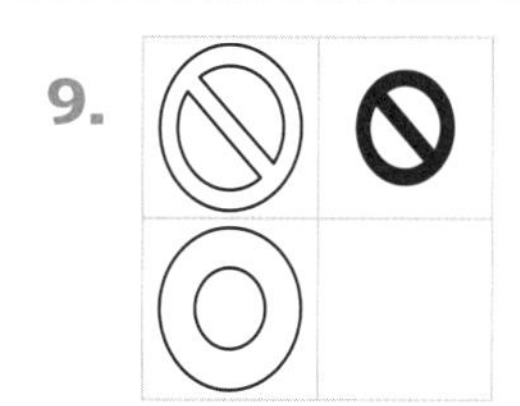

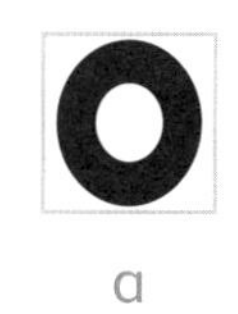
a

b

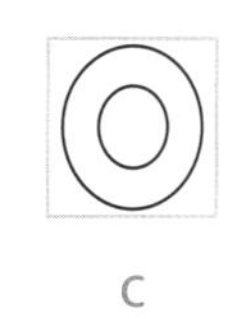
c

d

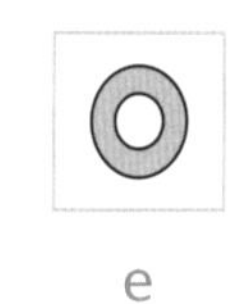
e

10.

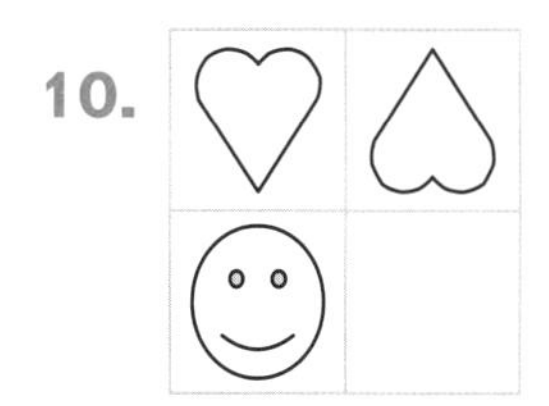

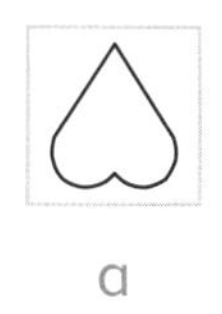
a

b

c

d

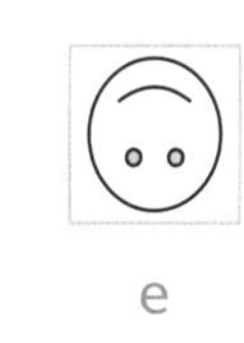
e

11.

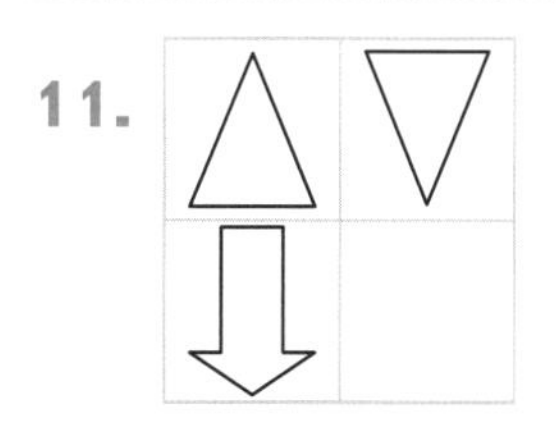

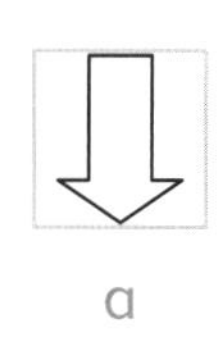
a

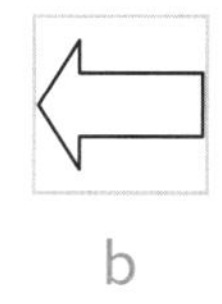
b

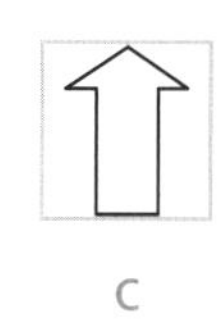
c

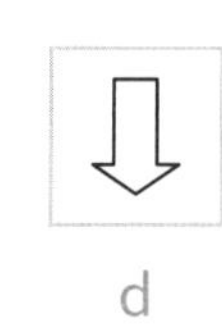
d

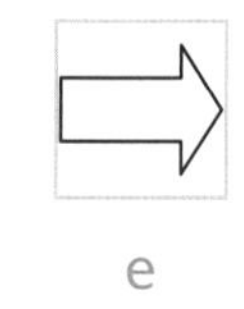
e

12.

a

b

c

d

e

End of test

Score:		**Time taken:**		**Target met?**	

Target time: **6 minutes**

Which picture on the right belongs to the group on the left? Circle the letter.

Example

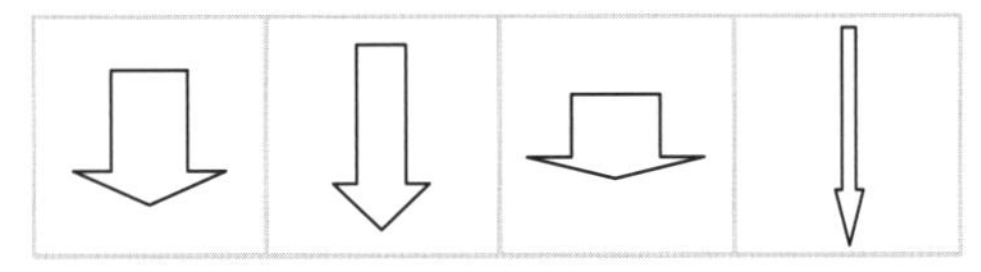

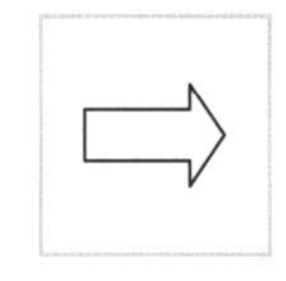 a 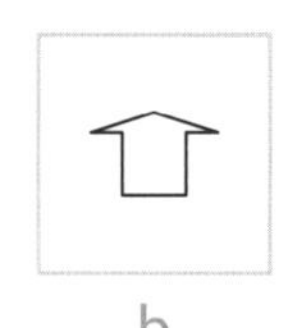 b 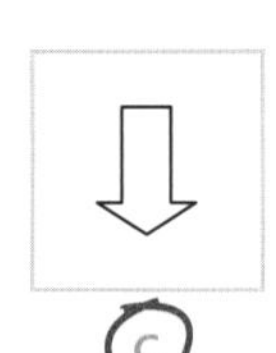 c 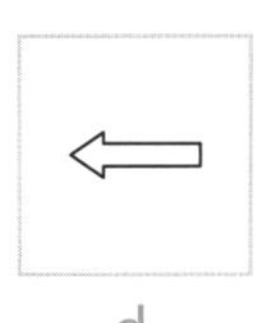 d 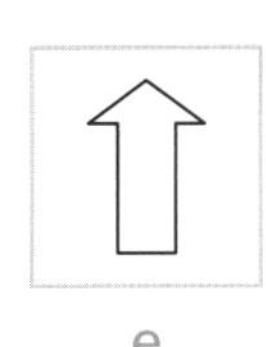 e

1.

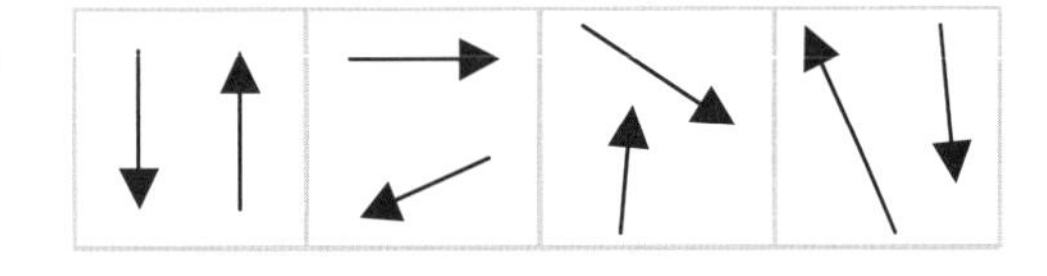

 a 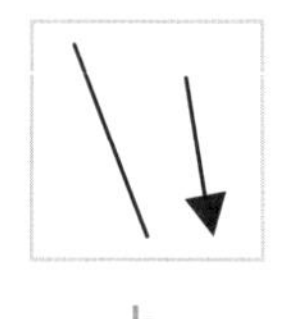 b  c 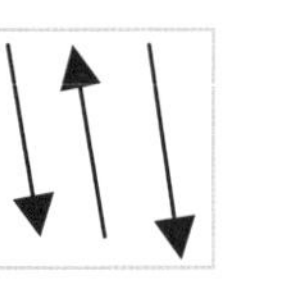 d 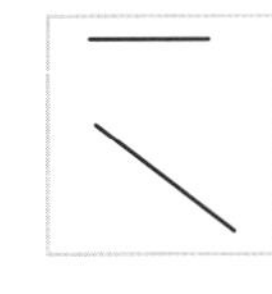 e

2.

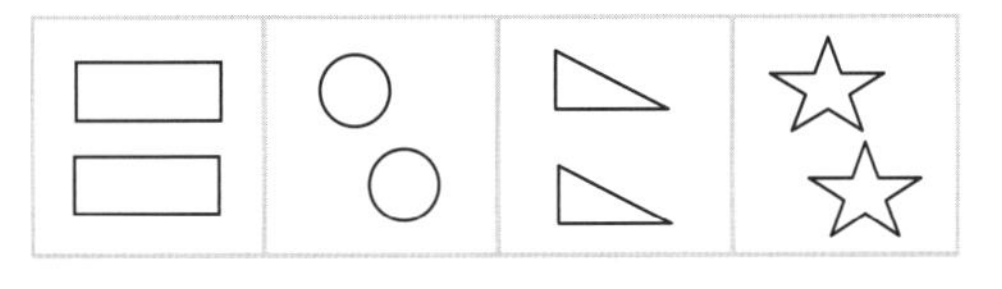

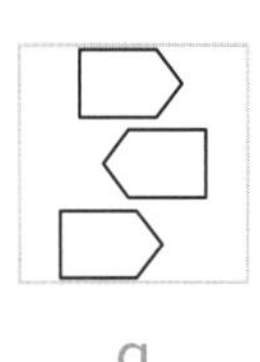 a 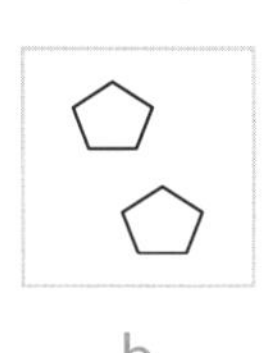 b 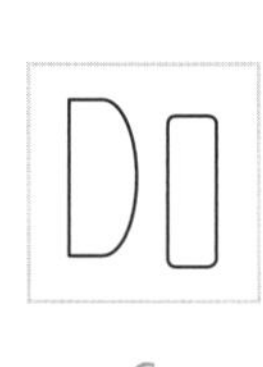 c 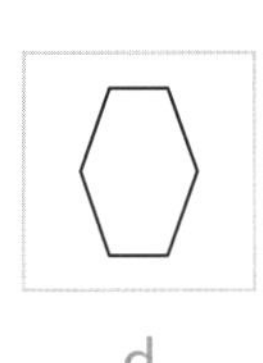 d  e

3.

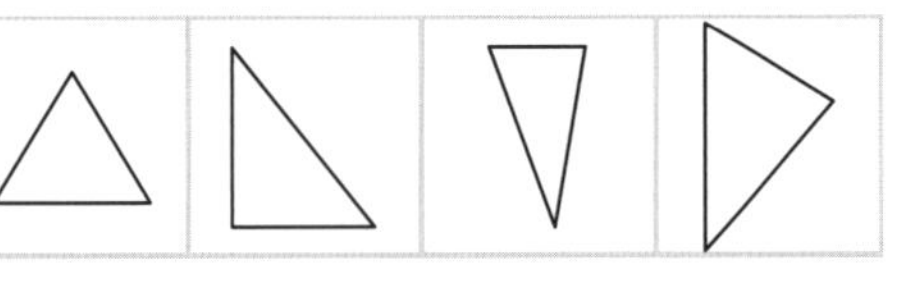

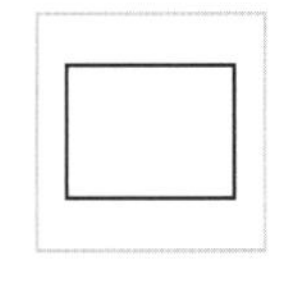 a 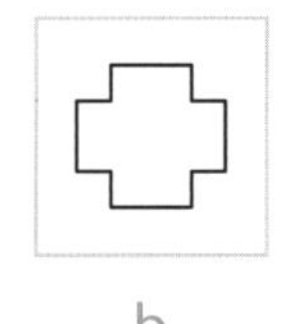 b  c 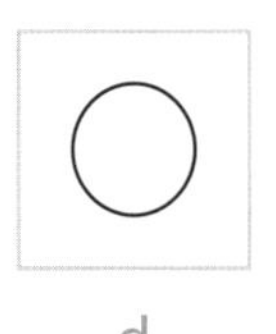 d 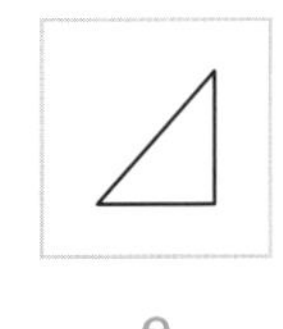 e

4.

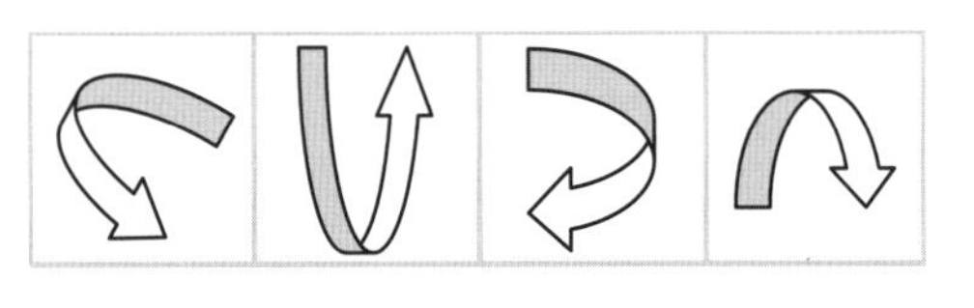

 a  b  c 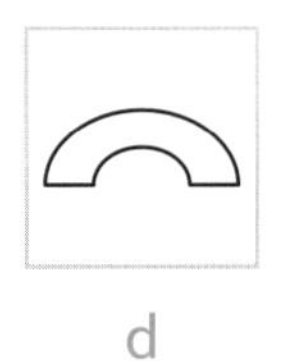 d  e

5.

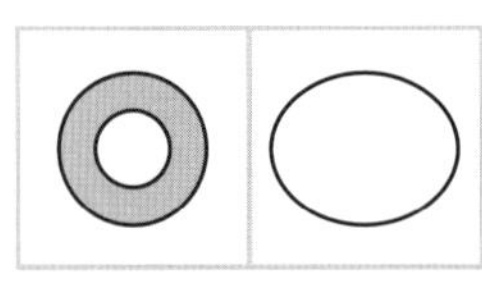  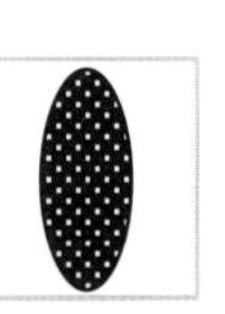

 a 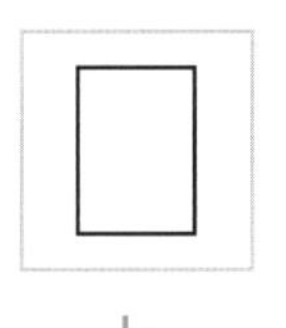 b 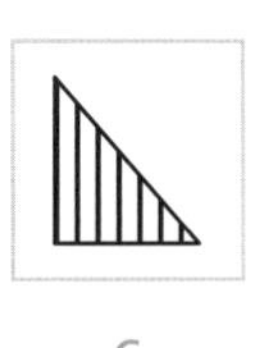 c 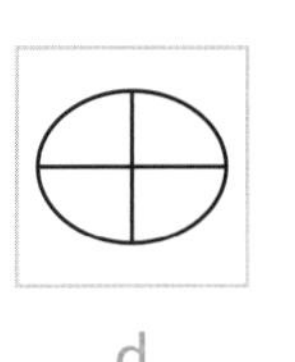 d 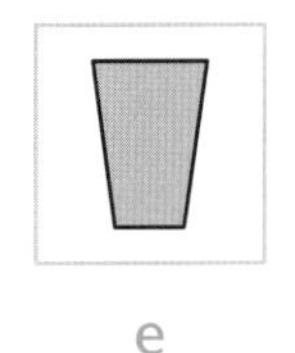 e

6.

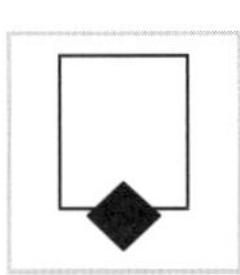 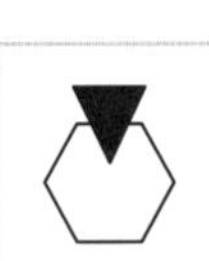 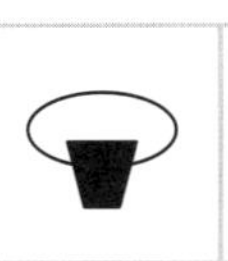 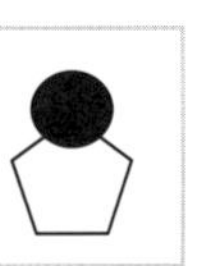

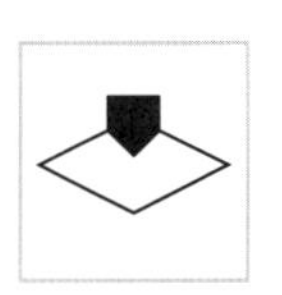 a b  c 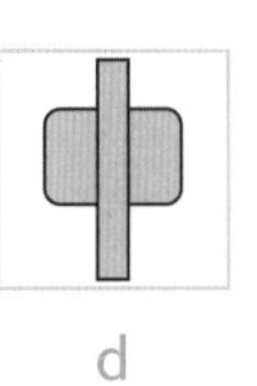 d  e

Now go on to the next page

Which picture is the odd one out? Circle the letter.

Example

				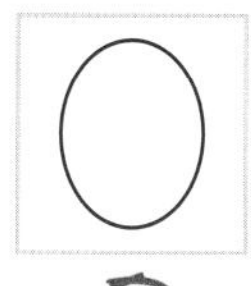
a	b	c	d	e

7.

	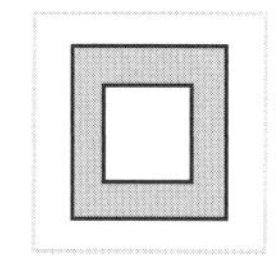	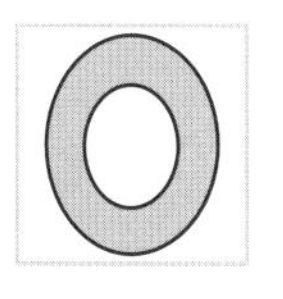		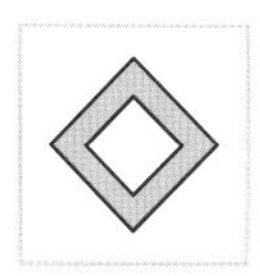
a	b	c	d	e

8.

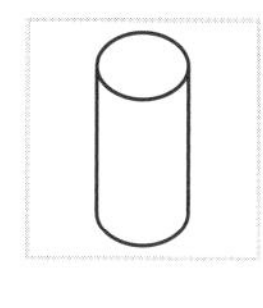	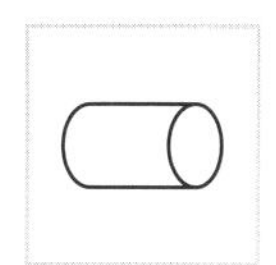	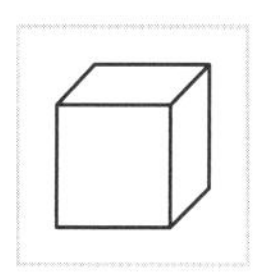	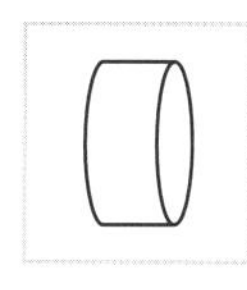	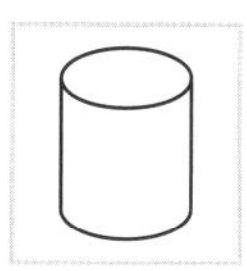
a	b	c	d	e

9.

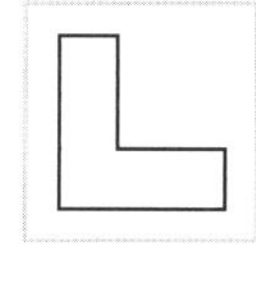	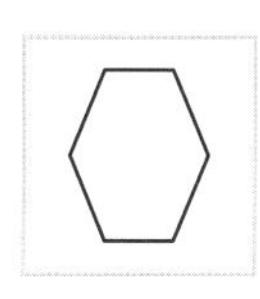	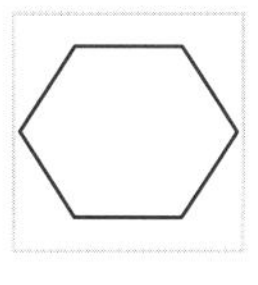	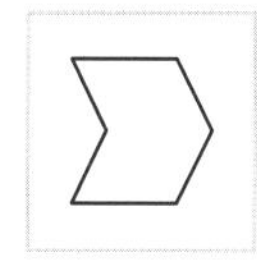	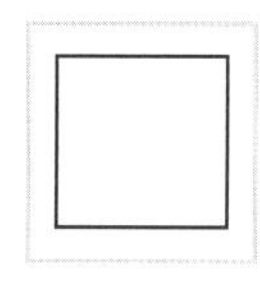
a	b	c	d	e

10.

a	b	c	d	e

11.

			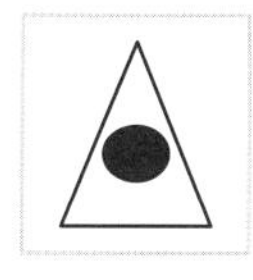	
a	b	c	d	e

12.

a	b	c	d	e

End of test

Score:		**Time taken:**		**Target met?**	

Target time: **6 minutes**

Which picture is the odd one out? Circle the letter.

Example

    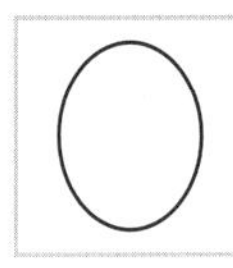

a b c d e

1.

a b c d e

2.

   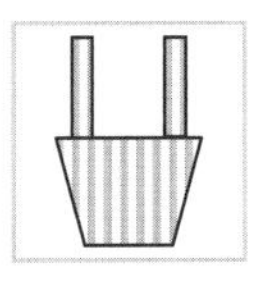 

a b c d e

3.

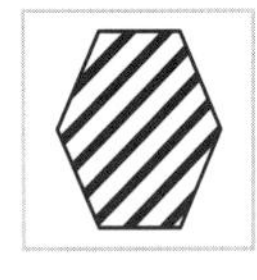   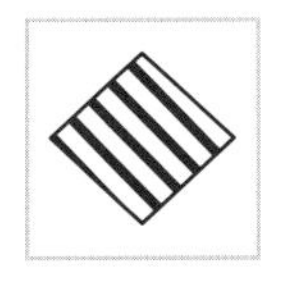 

a b c d e

4.

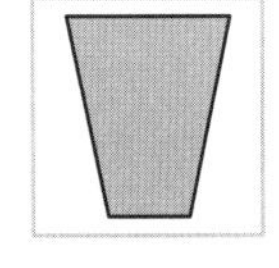  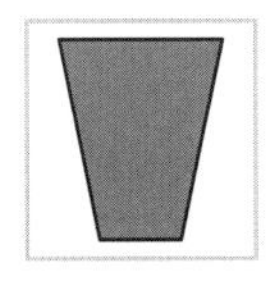  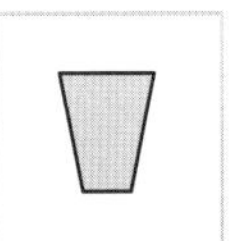

a b c d e

5.

a b c d e

6.

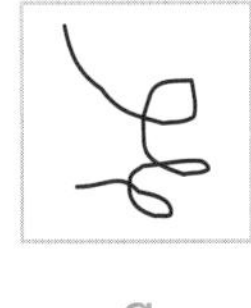 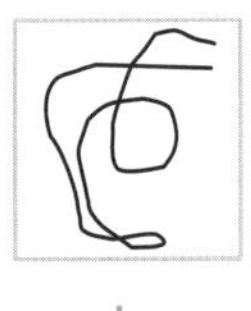 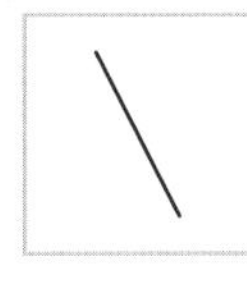 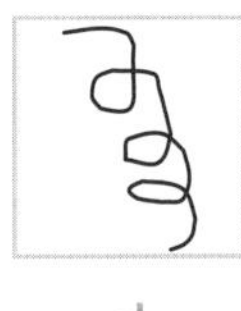 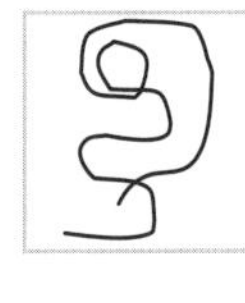

a b c d e

Now go on to the next page 

The first two pictures go together. Which of the five pictures on the right goes with the third picture in the same way? Circle the letter.

Example

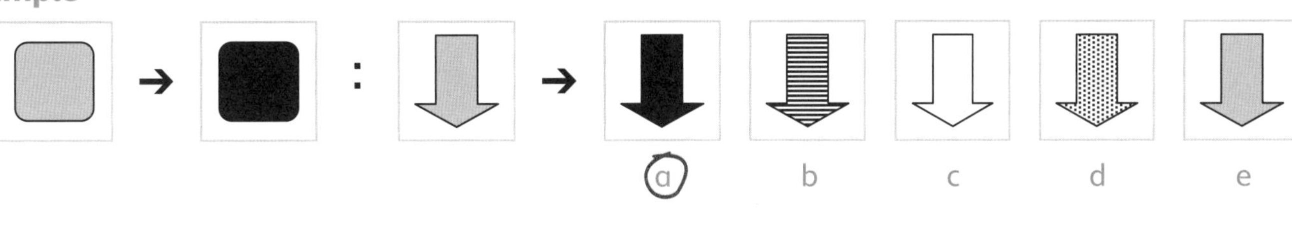

a b c d e

7.

a b c d e

8.

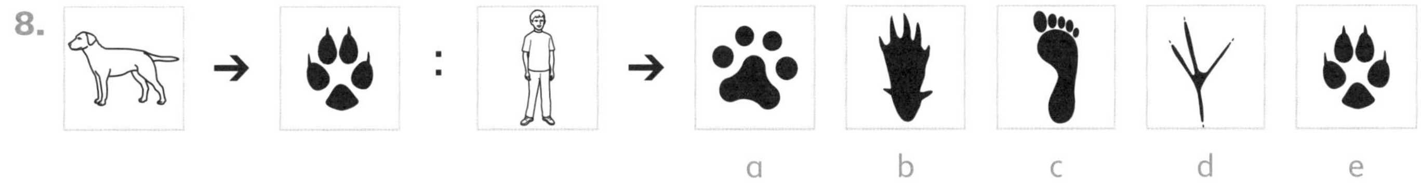

a b c d e

9.

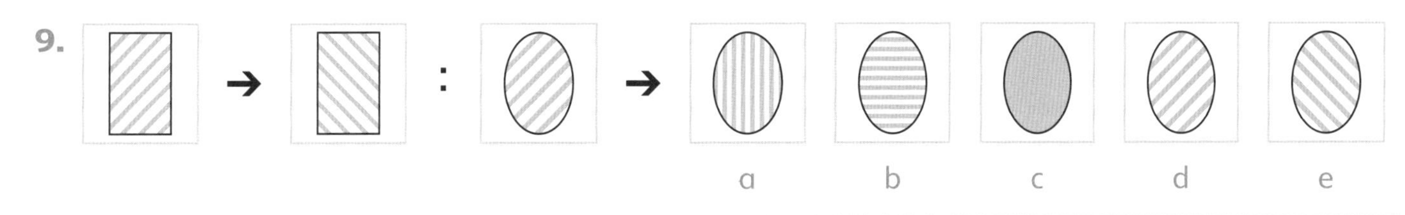

a b c d e

10.

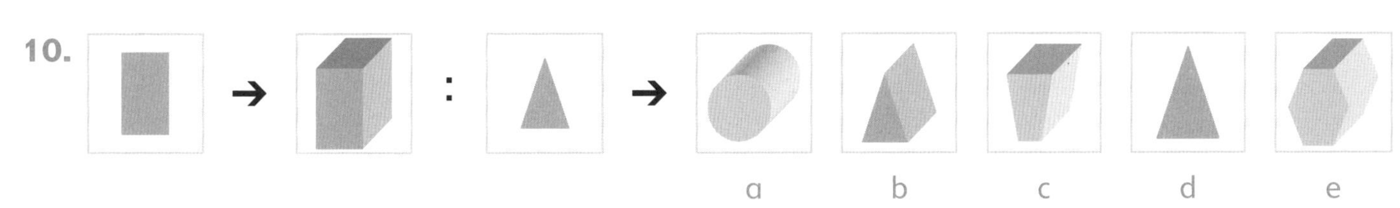

a b c d e

11.

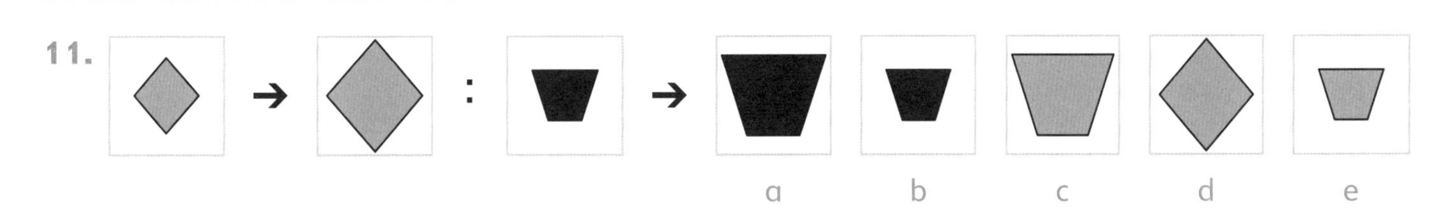

a b c d e

12.

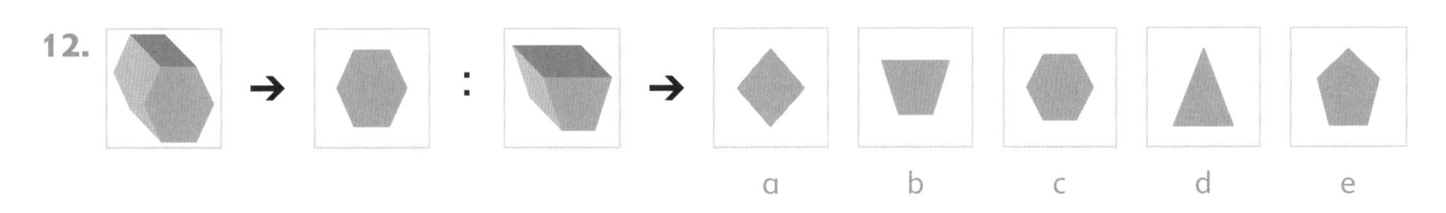

a b c d e

End of test

Score:		**Time taken:**		**Target met?**	

Target time: **6 minutes**

The first two pictures go together. Which of the five pictures on the right goes with the third picture in the same way? Circle the letter.

Example

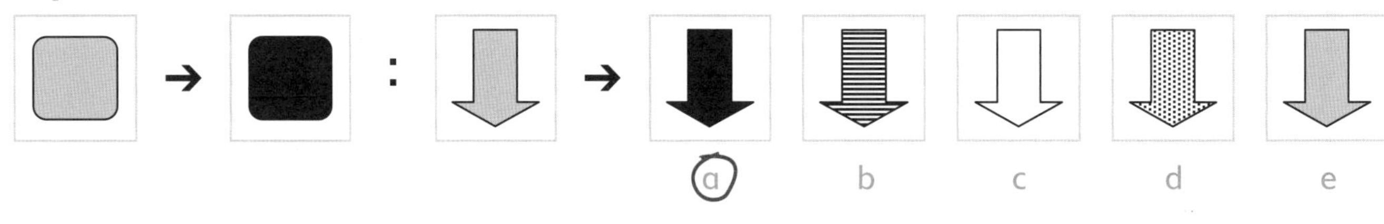

a b c d e

1.

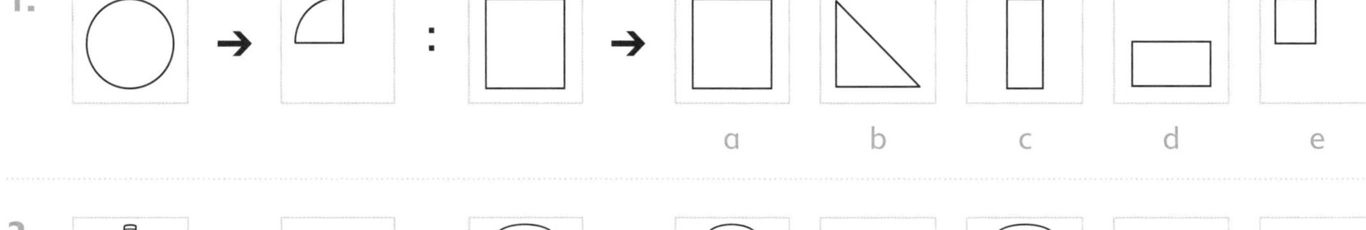

a b c d e

2.

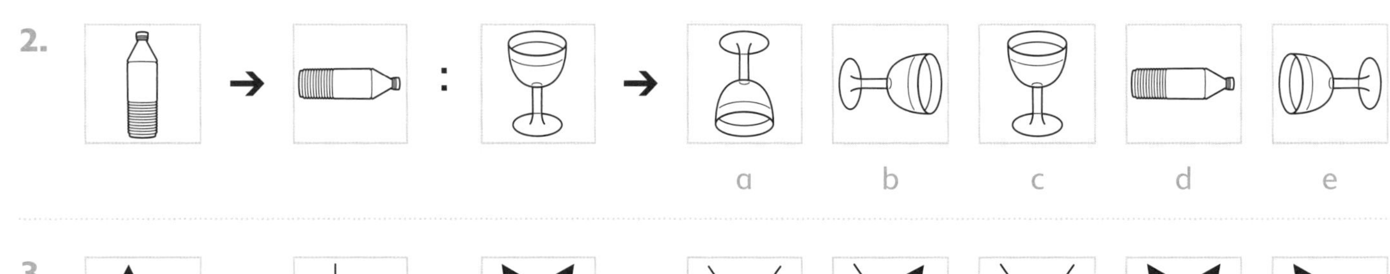

a b c d e

3.

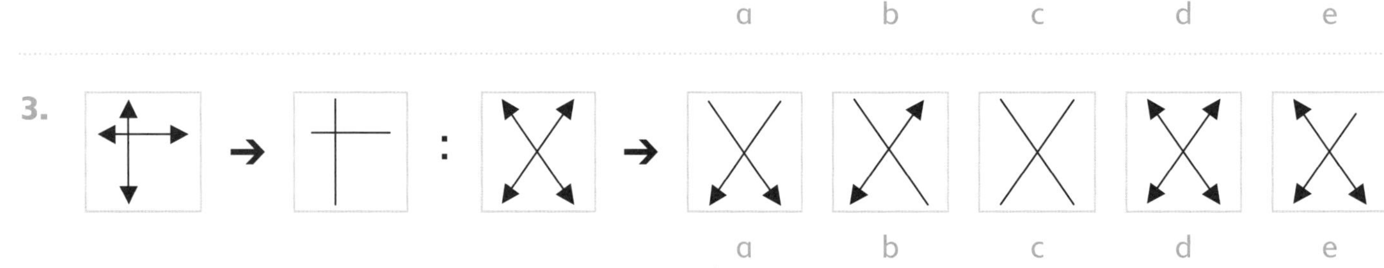

a b c d e

4.

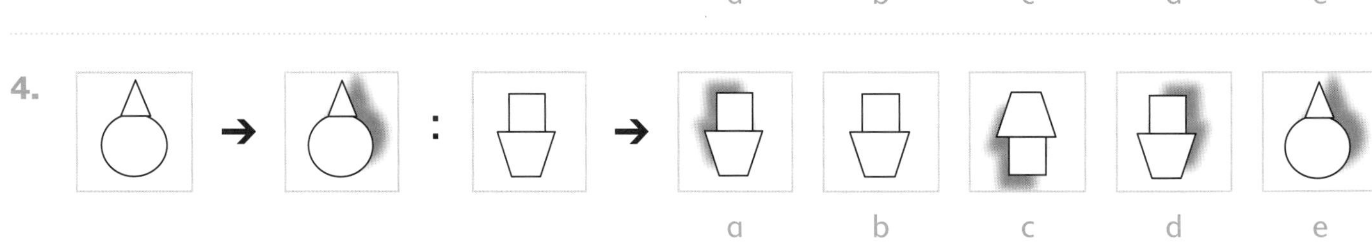

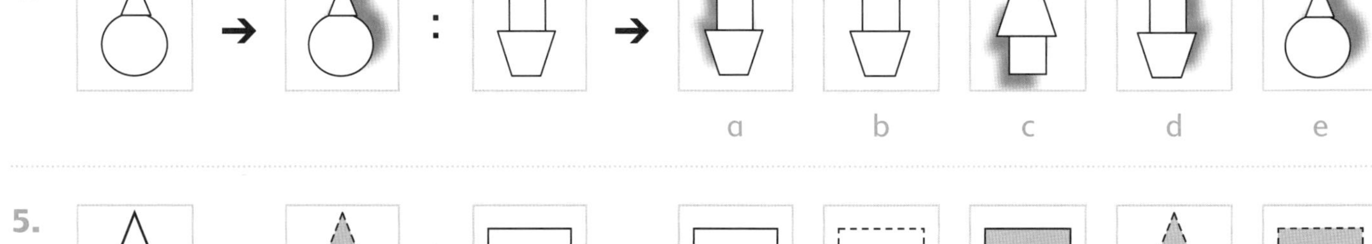

a b c d e

5.

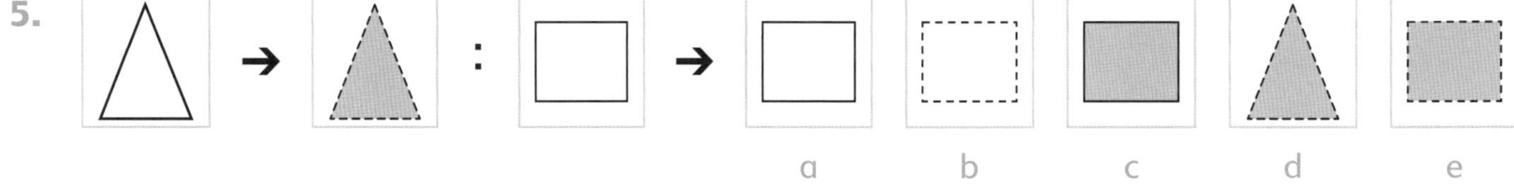

a b c d e

6.

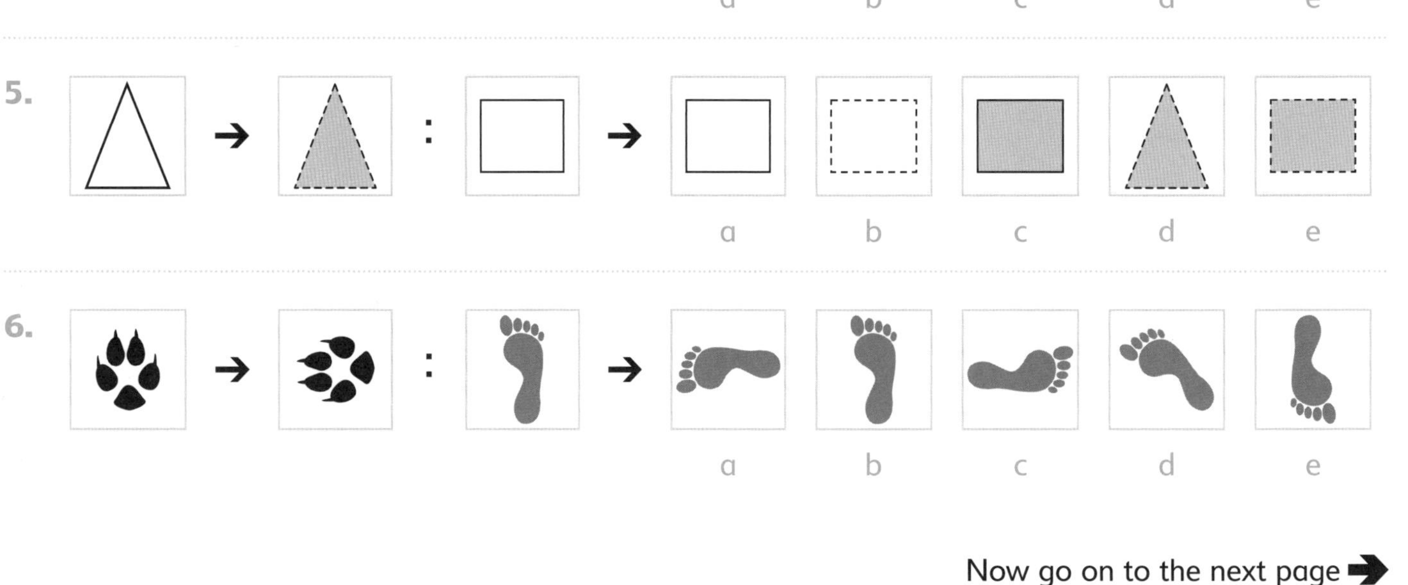

a b c d e

Now go on to the next page 

Which picture on the right belongs to the group on the left? Circle the letter.

Example

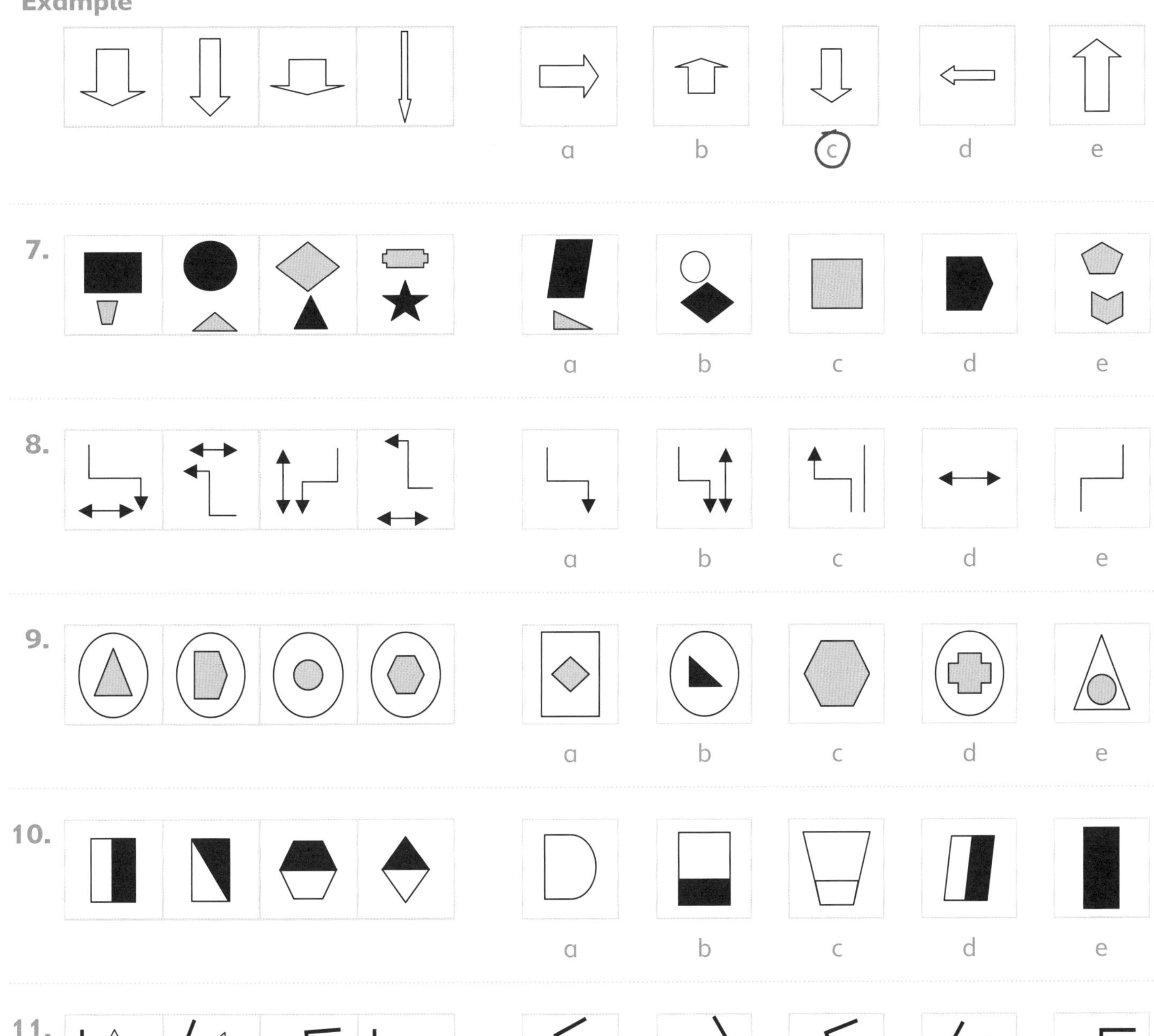

12.

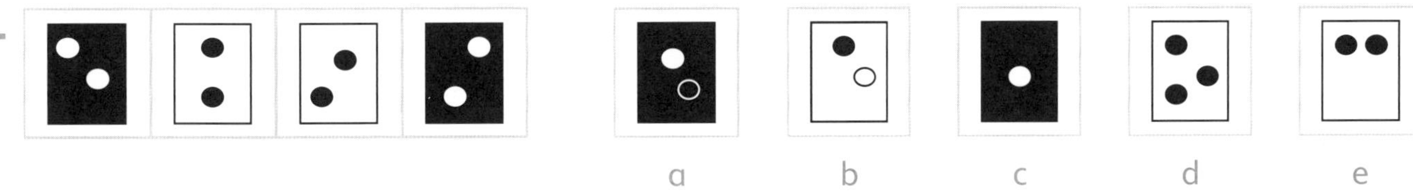

End of test

Score:		Time taken:		Target met?	

Target time: **6 minutes**

In which picture on the right is the picture on the left hidden? Circle the letter.

Example

    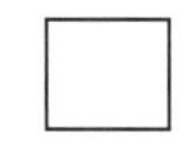 

a b c d e

1.   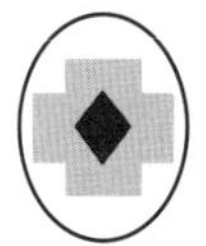  

a b c d e

2.      

a b c d e

3.      

a b c d e

4. 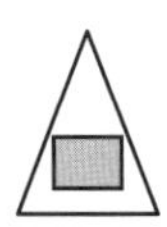  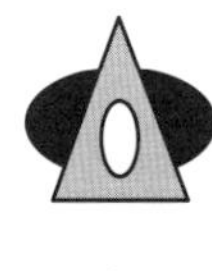  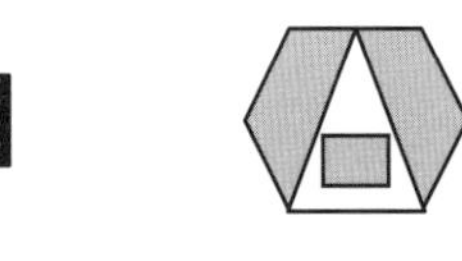

a b c d e

5.     

a b c d e

6. 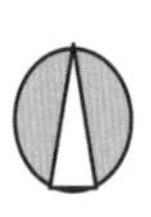 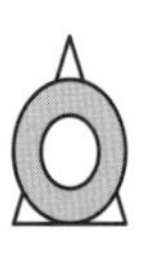 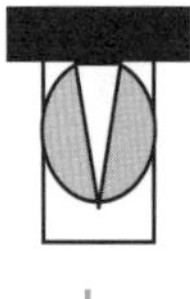   

a b c d e

Now go on to the next page

Pretend the dotted line is a mirror. Which picture on the right is a reflection of the picture on the left? Circle the letter.

Example

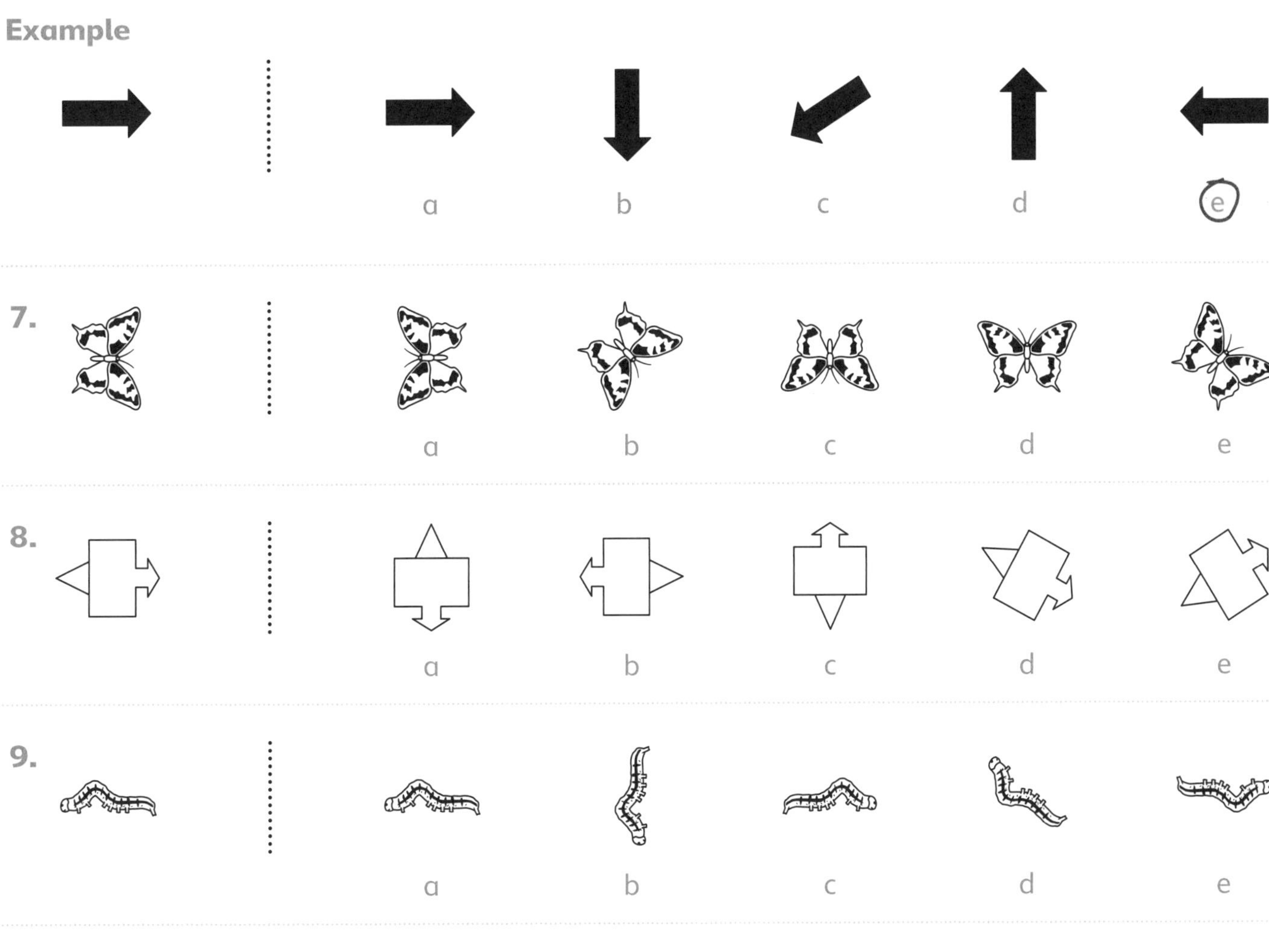

a b c d e

7. a b c d e

8. a b c d e

9. a b c d e

10.   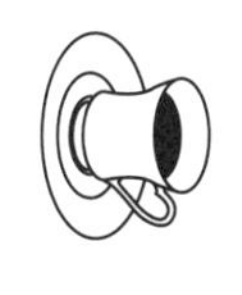     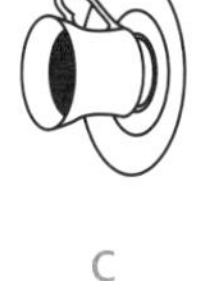  

a b c d e

11. 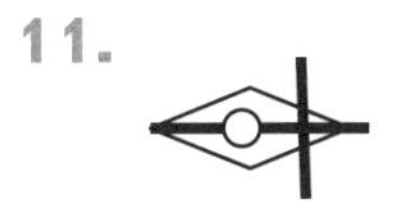  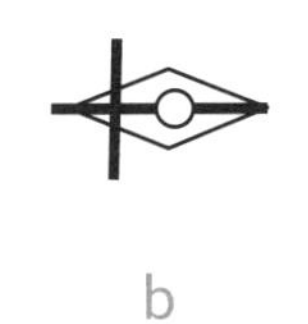   

a b c d e

12.  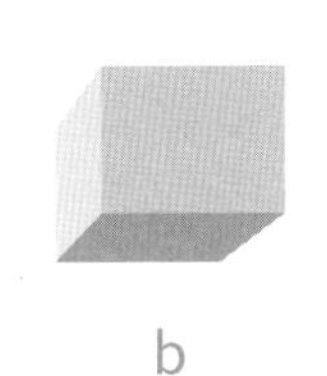 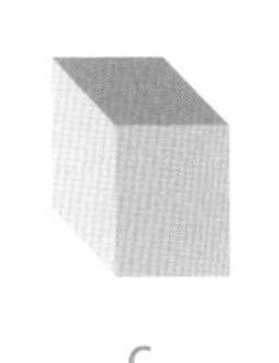  

a b c d e

End of test

Score:		Time taken:		Target met?	

Target time: **6 minutes**

Pretend the dotted line is a mirror. Which picture on the right is a reflection of the picture on the left? Circle the letter.

Example

a b c d e

1.      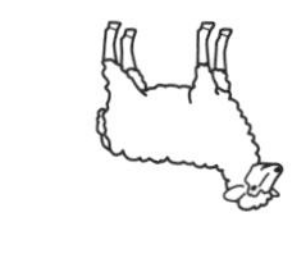 

a b c d e

2.      

a b c d e

3.       

a b c d e

4.        

a b c d e

5.      

a b c d e

6.     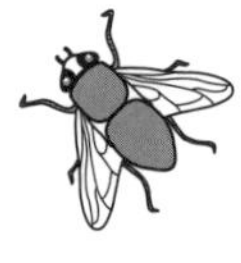  

a b c d e

Now go on to the next page ➔

Which of the pictures on the right best fits into the space in the grid? Circle the letter.

Example

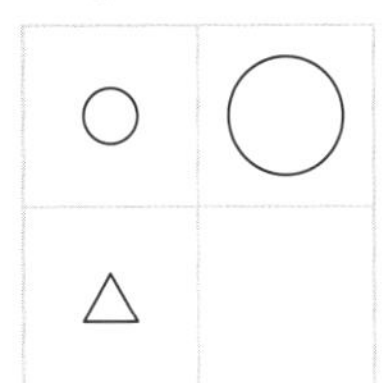

 a
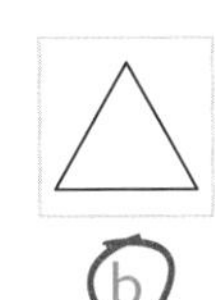 b
 c
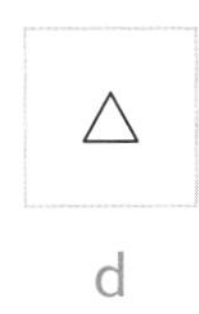 d
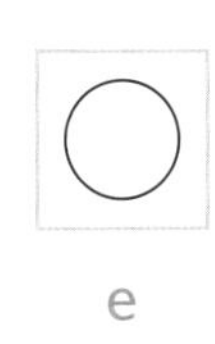 e

7.

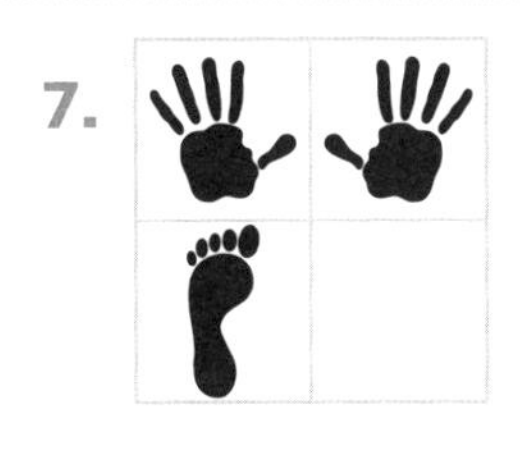

 a
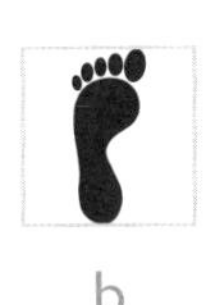 b
 c
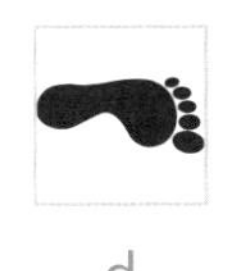 d
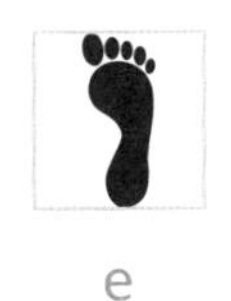 e

8.

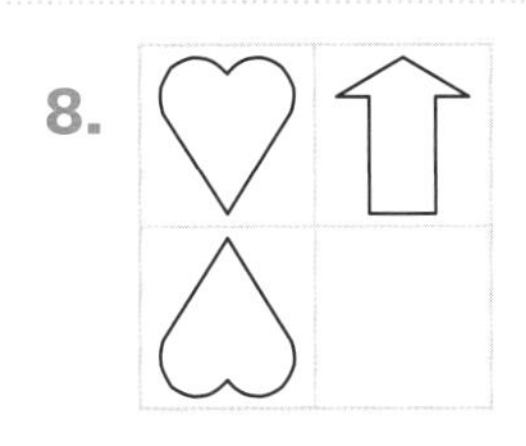

 a
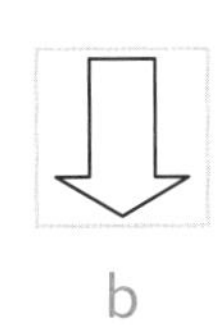 b
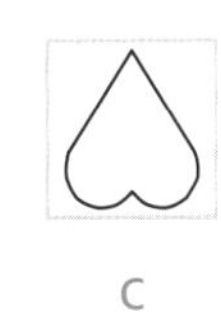 c
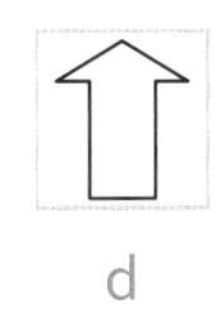 d
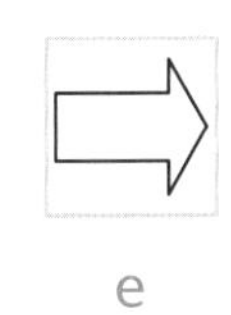 e

9.

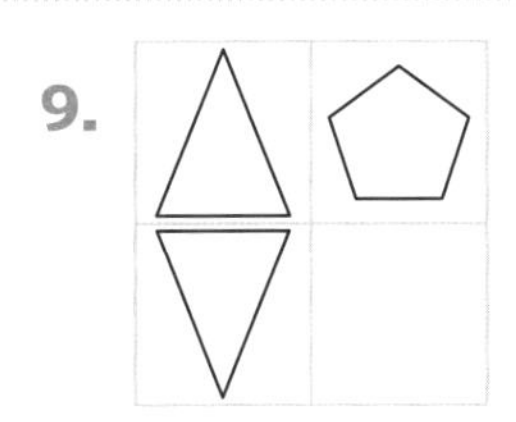

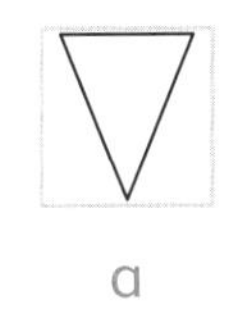 a
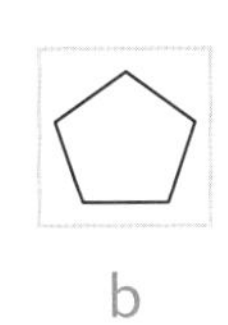 b
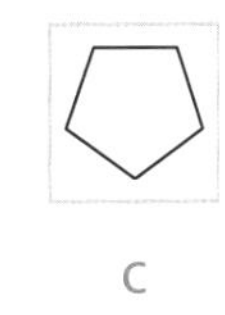 c
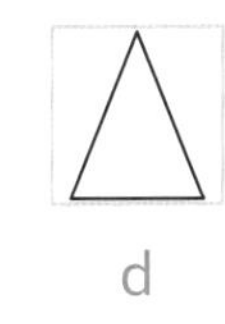 d
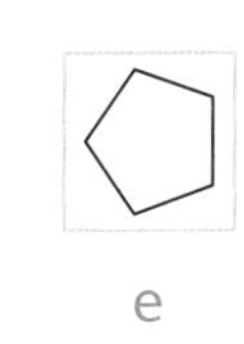 e

10.

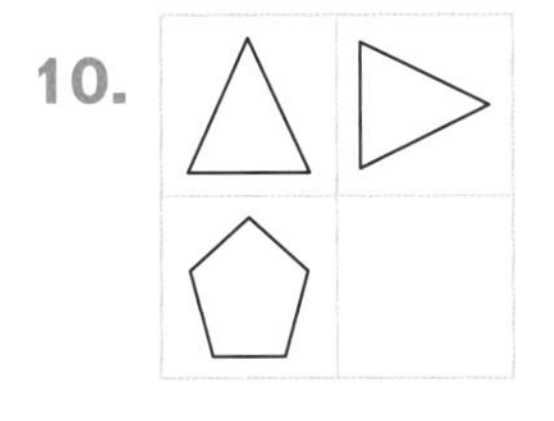

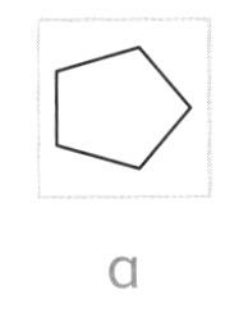 a
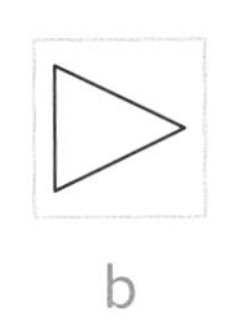 b
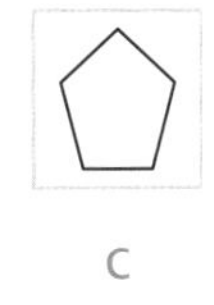 c
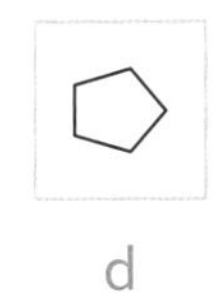 d
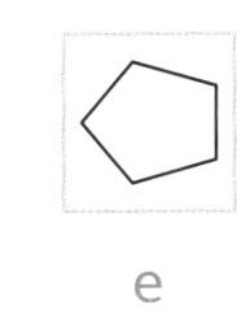 e

11.

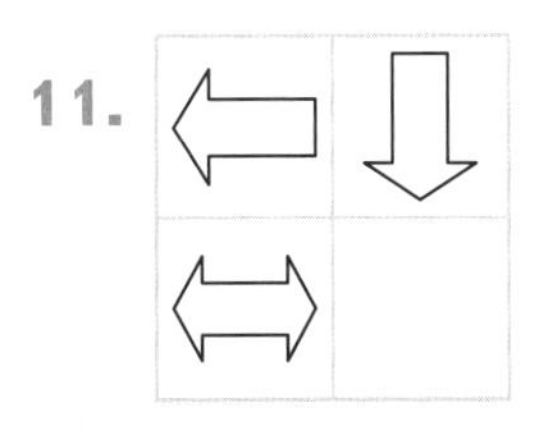

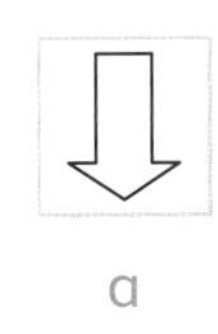 a
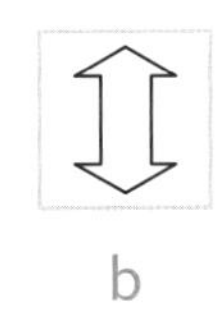 b
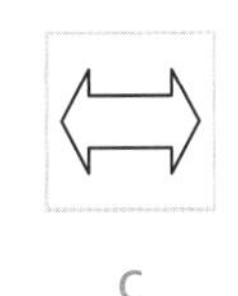 c
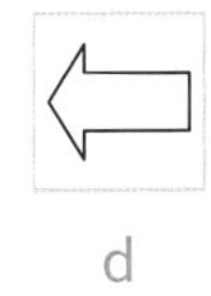 d
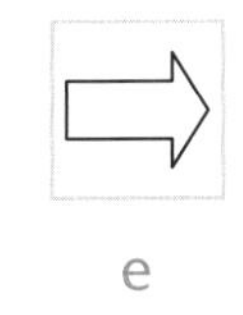 e

12.

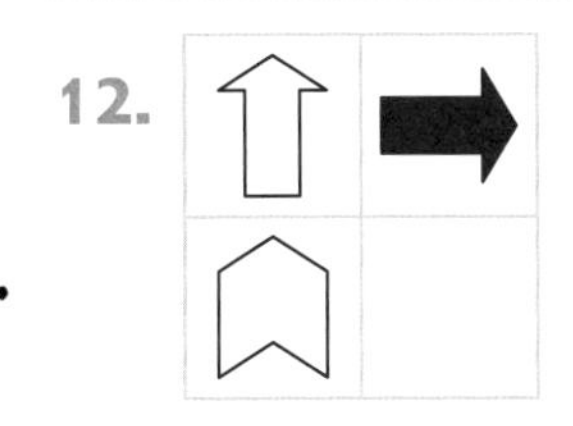

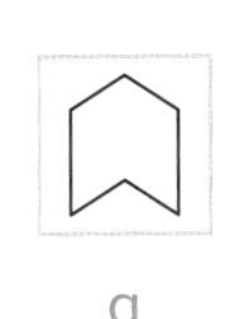 a
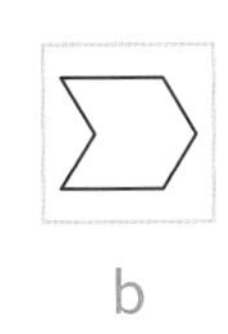 b
 c
 d
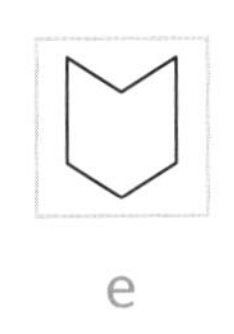 e

End of test

Score:		**Time taken:**		**Target met?**	

Target time: **6 minutes**

Which of the pictures on the right best fits into the space in the grid? Circle the letter.

Example

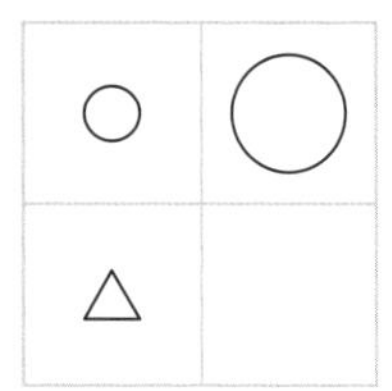

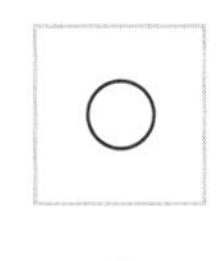 a

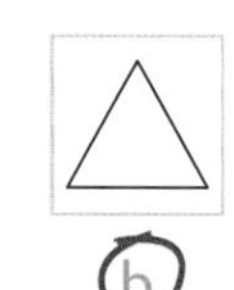 (b)

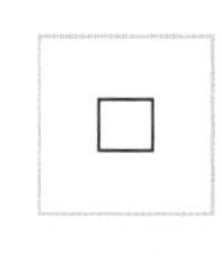 c

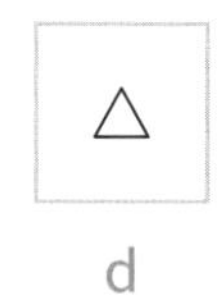 d

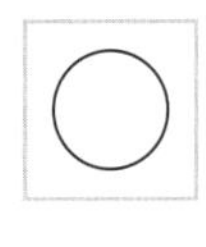 e

1.

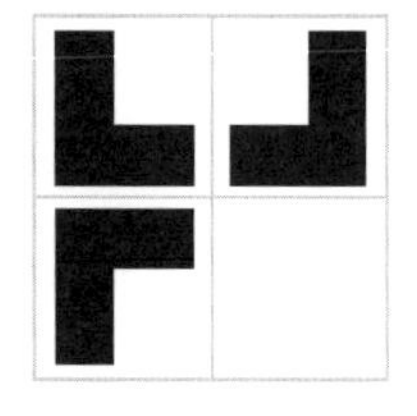

 a

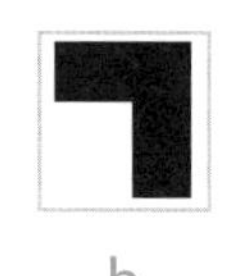 b

 c

 d

 e

2.

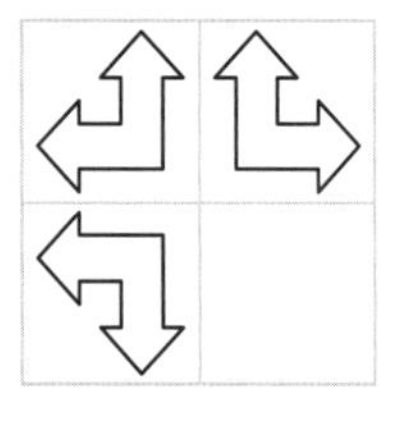

 a

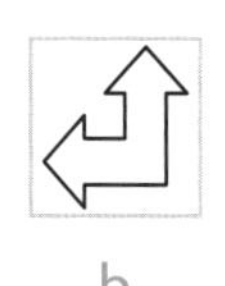 b

 c

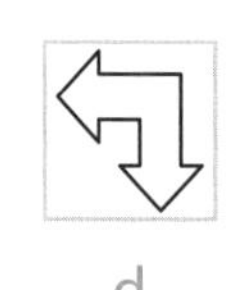 d

 e

3.

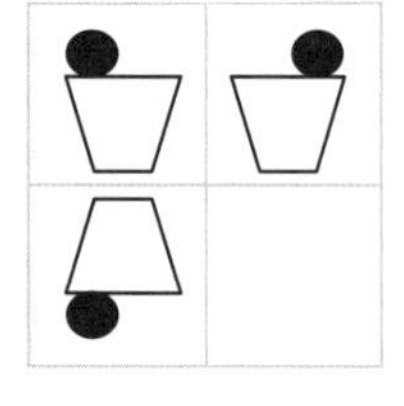

 a

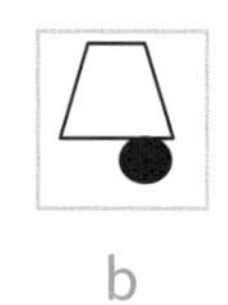 b

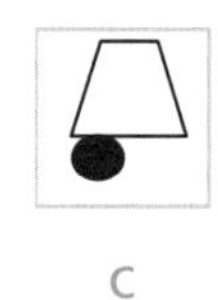 c

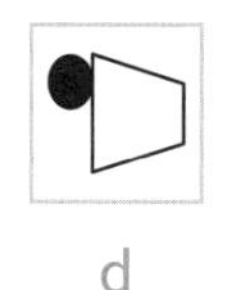 d

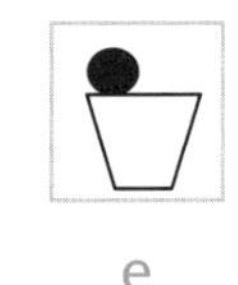 e

4.

 a

 b

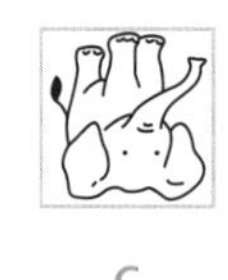 c

 d

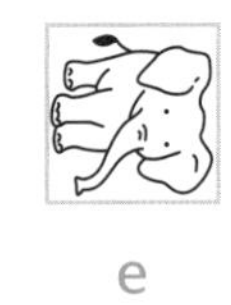 e

5.

 a

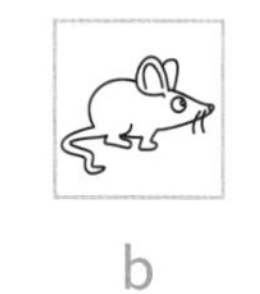 b

 c

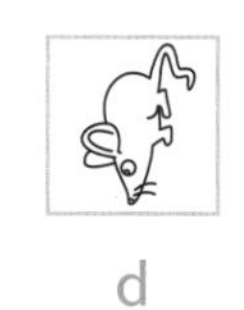 d

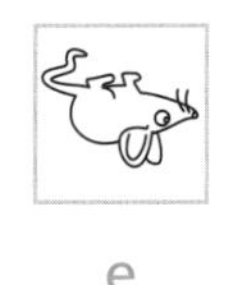 e

6.

 a

 b

 c

 d

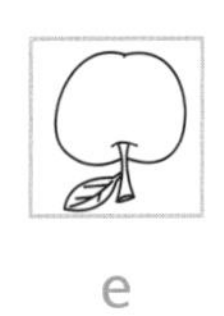 e

Now go on to the next page ➔

Which picture on the right goes in the empty space? Circle the letter.

Example

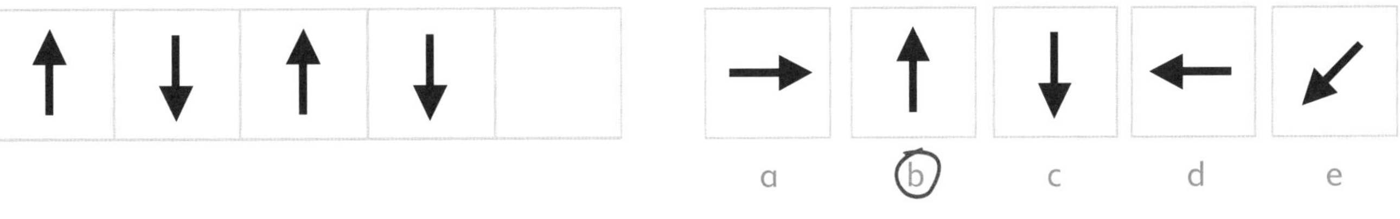

a b c d e

7. 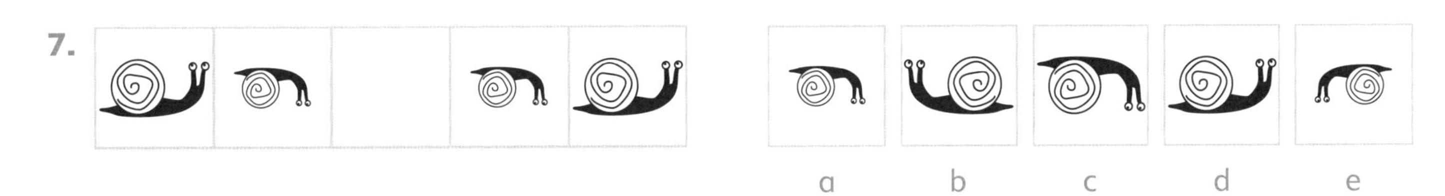

a b c d e

8. 

a b c d e

9. 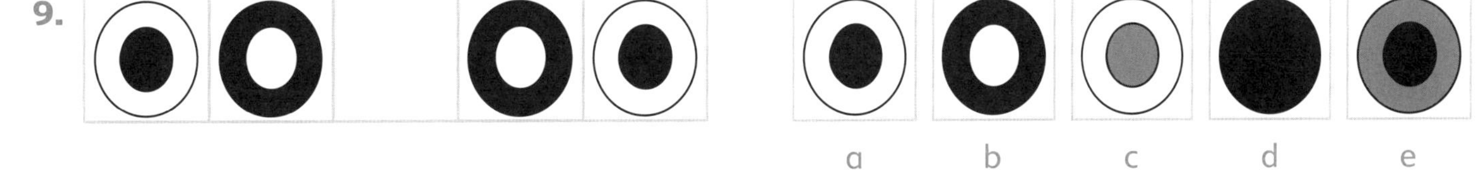

a b c d e

10. 

a b c d e

11. 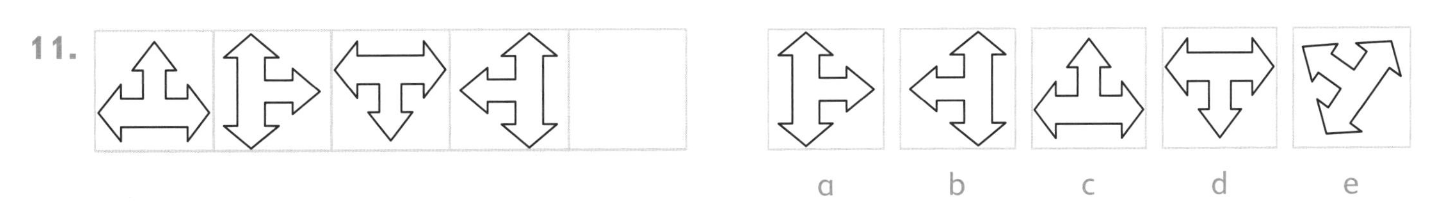

a b c d e

12. 

a b c d e

End of test

Score:		Time taken:		Target met?	

Target time: **6 minutes**

Which picture on the right belongs to the group on the left? Circle the letter.

Example

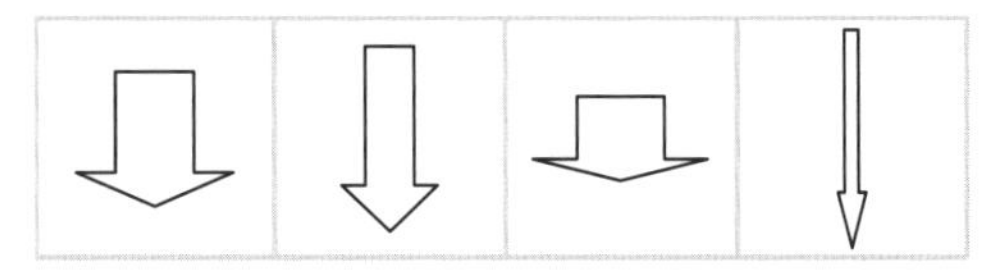

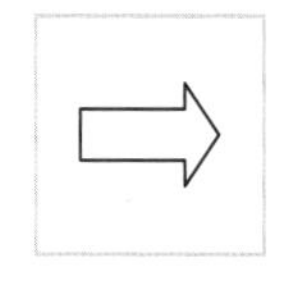 a
 b
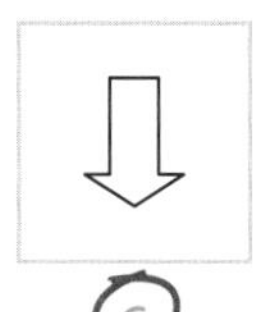 c
 d
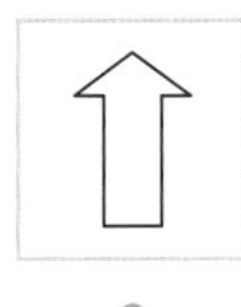 e

1.

 a
 b
 c
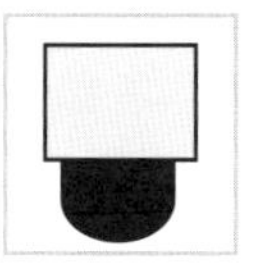 d
 e

2.

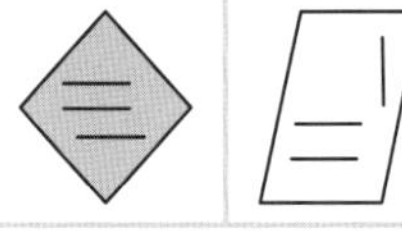

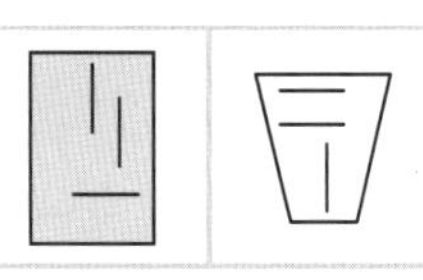

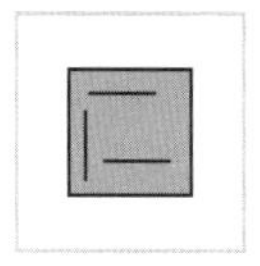 a
 b
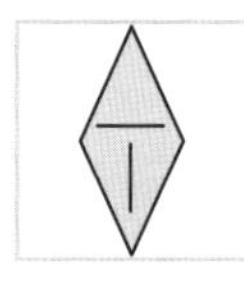 c
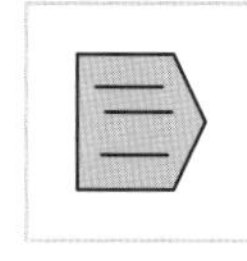 d
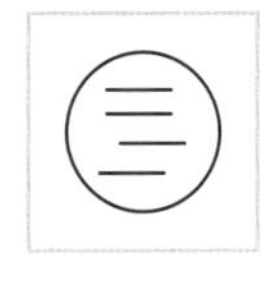 e

3.

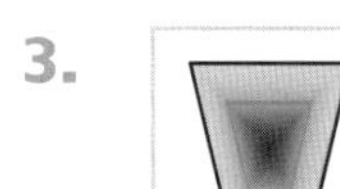
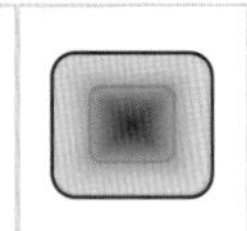
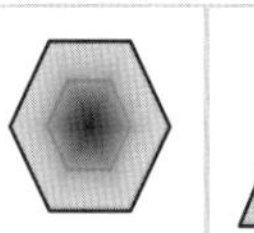
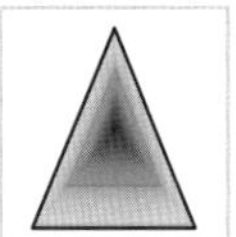

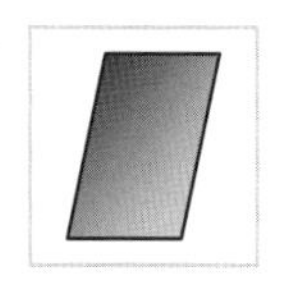 a
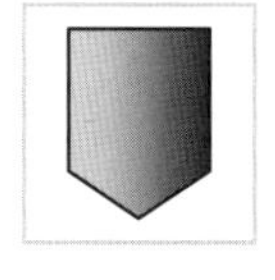 b
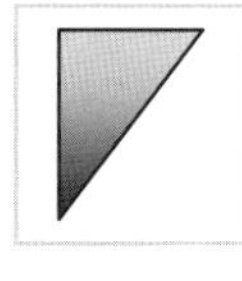 c
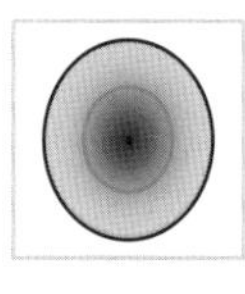 d
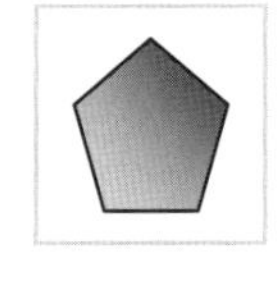 e

4.

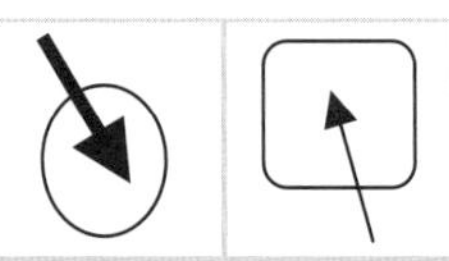
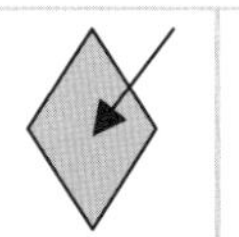

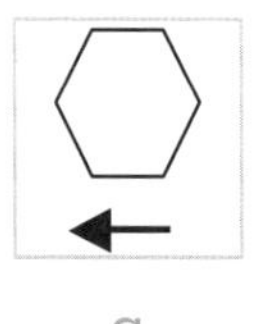 a
 b
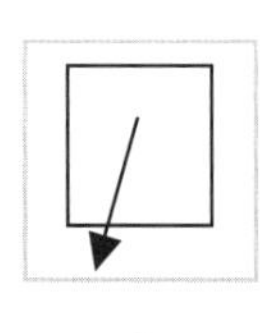 c
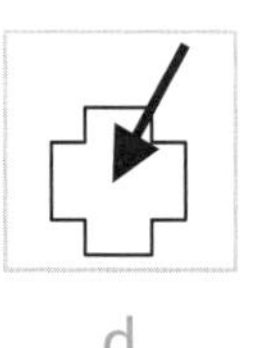 d
 e

5.

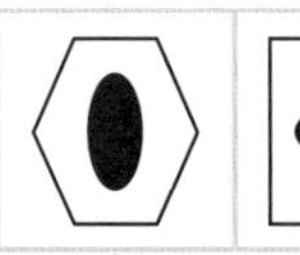

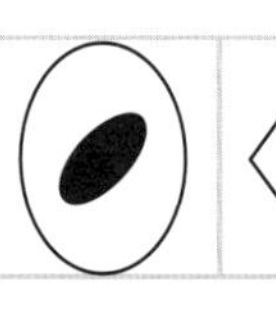
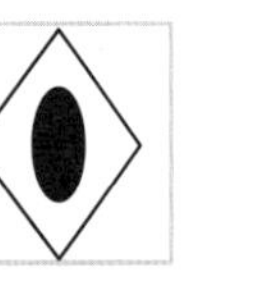

 a
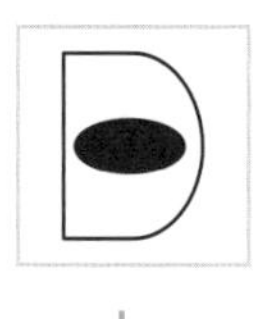 b
 c
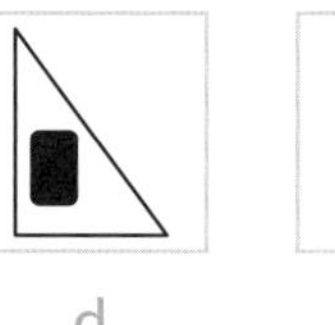 d
 e

6.

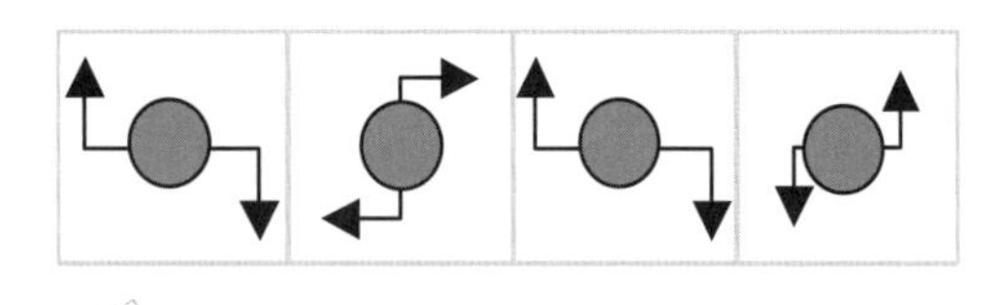

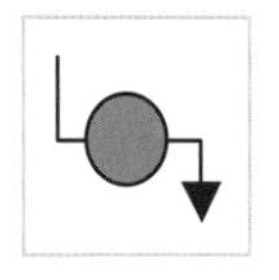 a
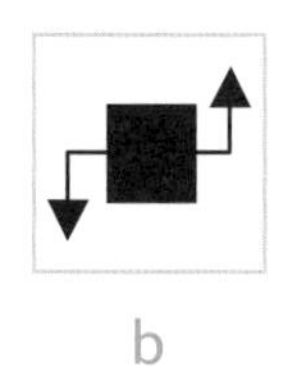 b
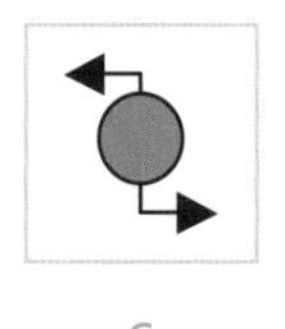 c
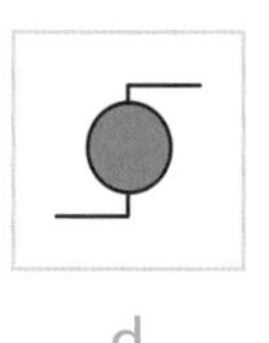 d
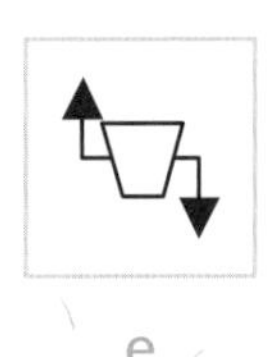 e

Now go on to the next page ➔

Which picture is the odd one out? Circle the letter.

Example

	a	b	c	d	e
Example					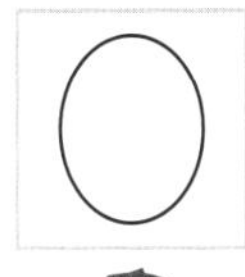
7.					
8.	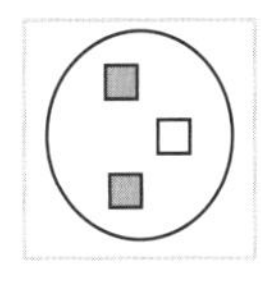	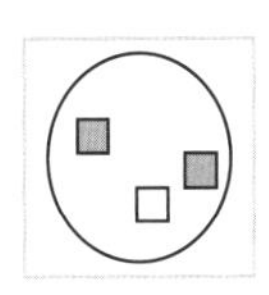	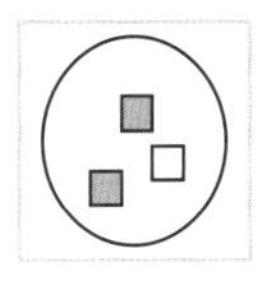	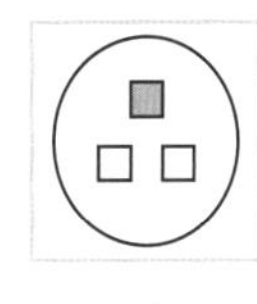	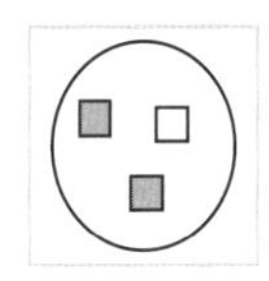
9.	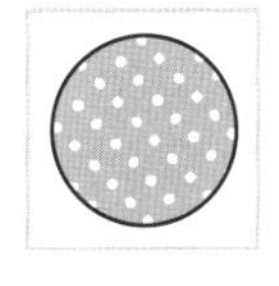	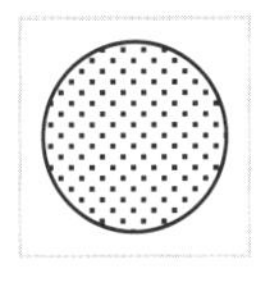	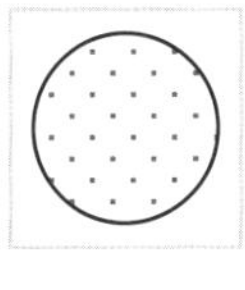		
10.					
11.	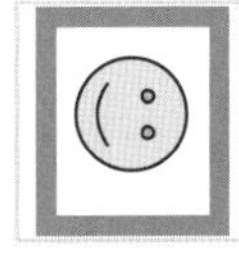	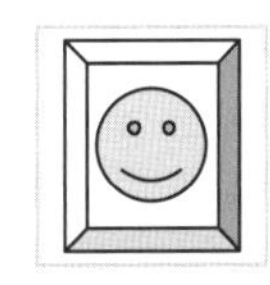	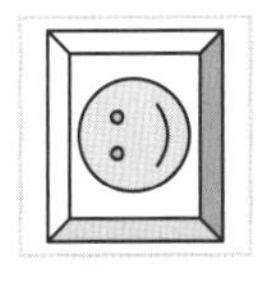	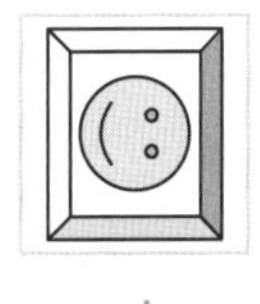	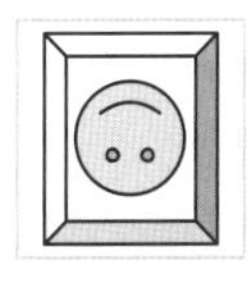
12.		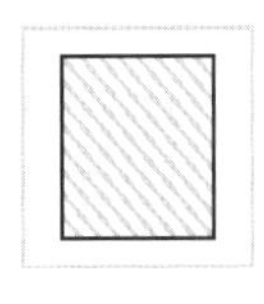	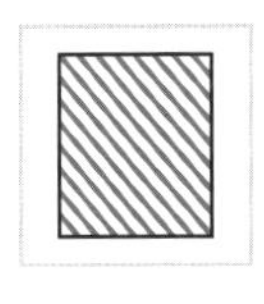	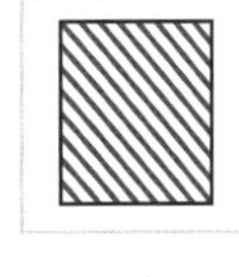	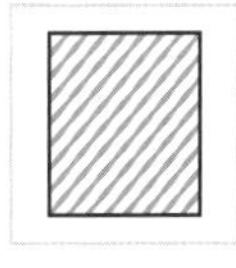

End of test

Score:		**Time taken:**		**Target met?**	

Target time: **6 minutes**

The first two pictures go together. Which of the five pictures on the right goes with the third picture in the same way? Circle the letter.

Example

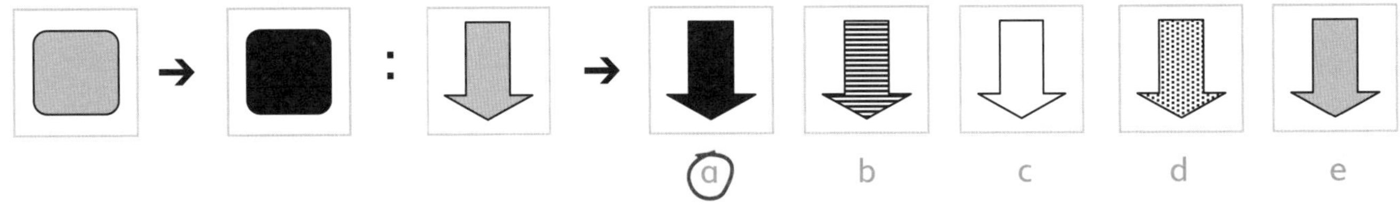

a b c d e

1.

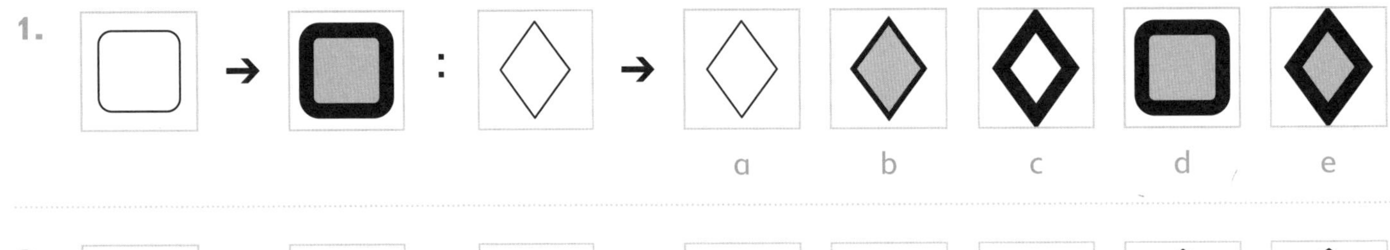

a b c d e

2.

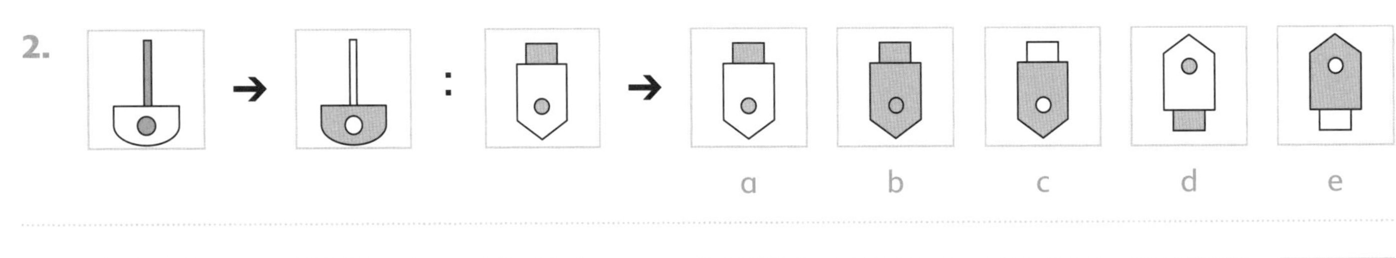

a b c d e

3.

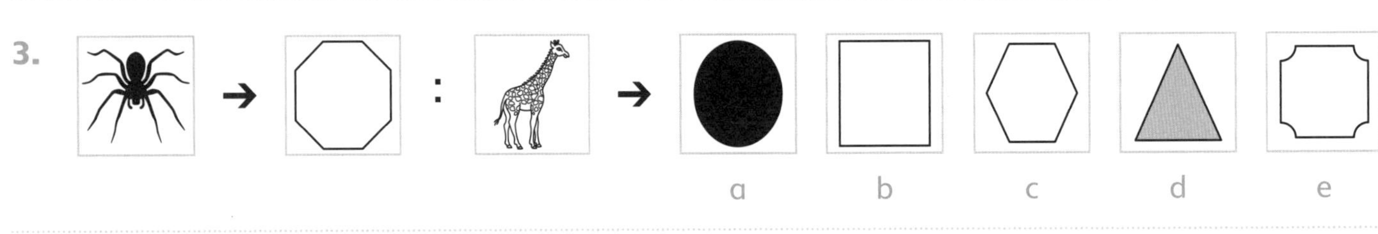

a b c d e

4.

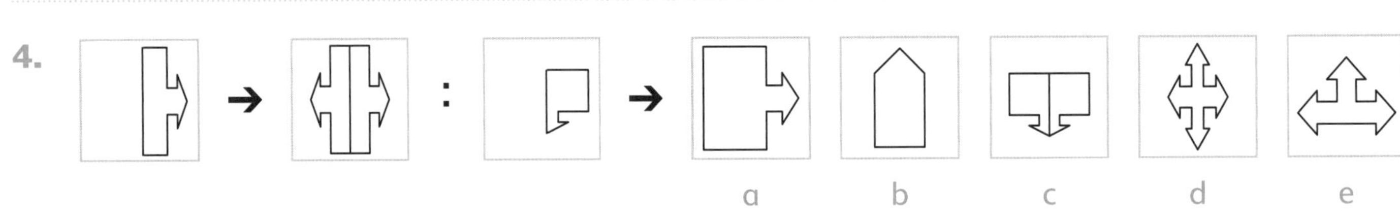

a b c d e

5.

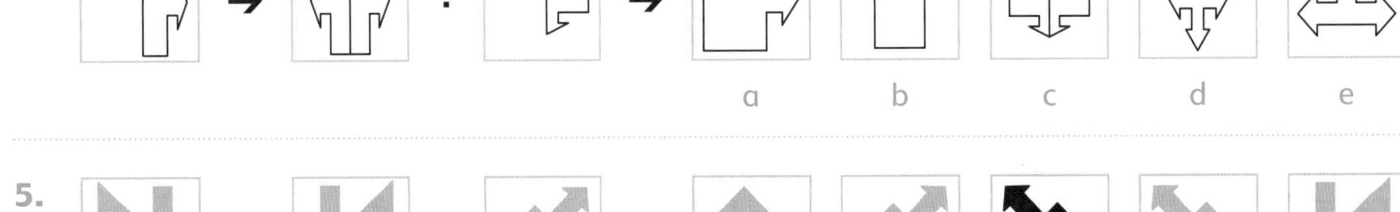

a b c d e

6.

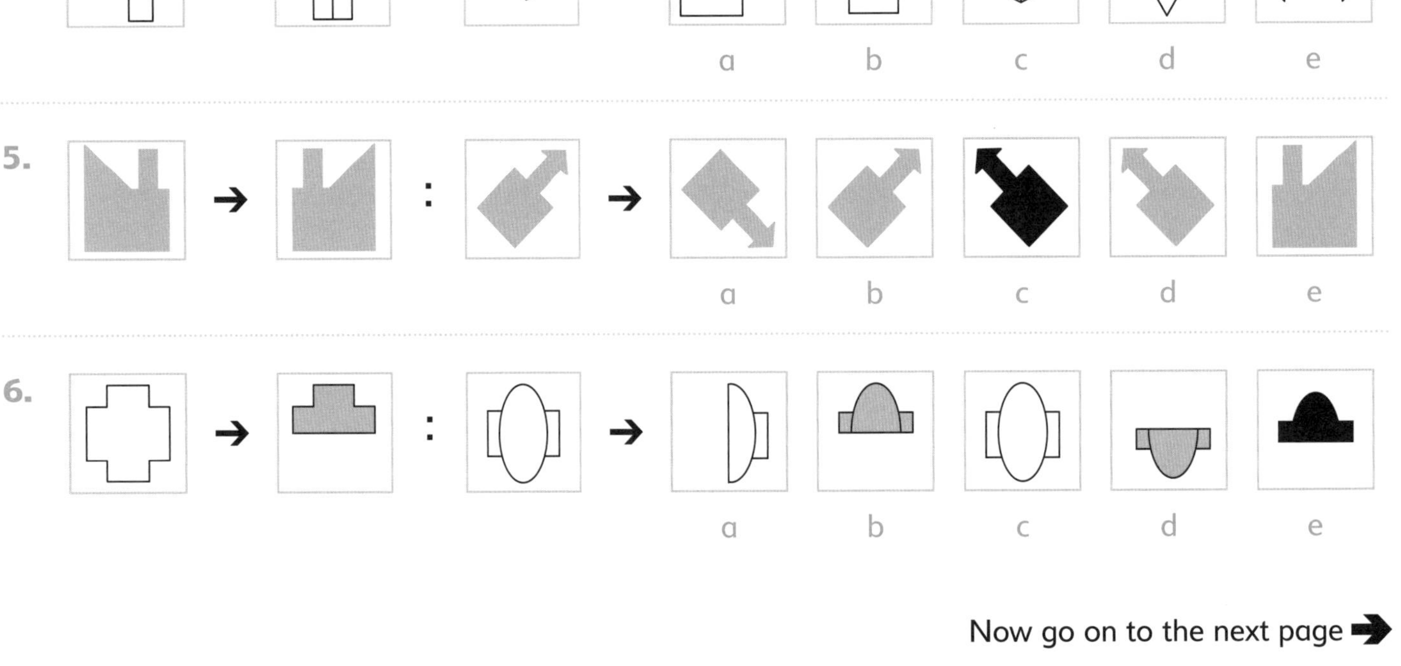

a b c d e

Now go on to the next page

Which picture on the right goes in the empty space? Circle the letter.

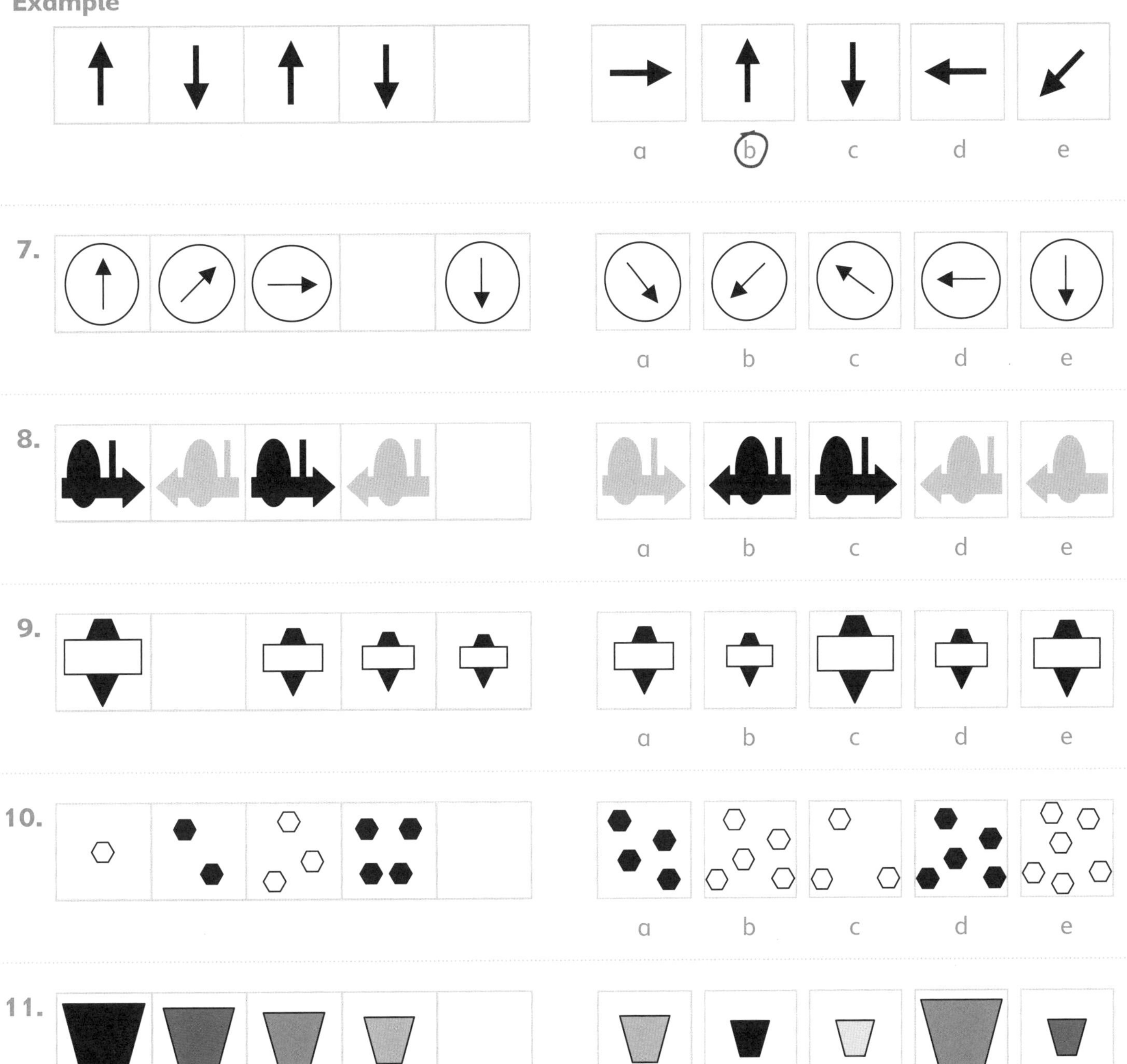

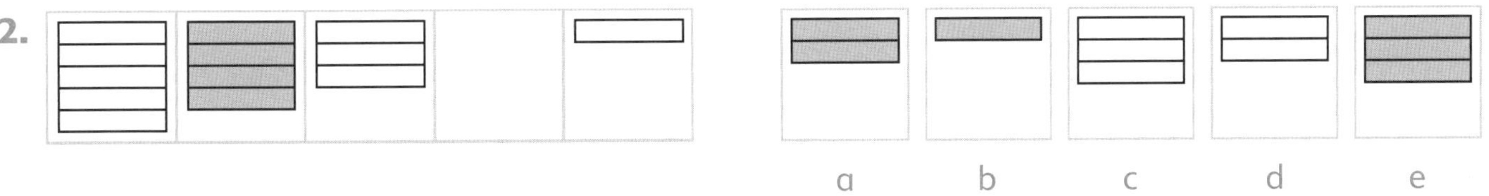

End of test

Score:		Time taken:		Target met?	

Target time: **6 minutes**

In which picture on the right is the picture on the left hidden? Circle the letter.

Example

    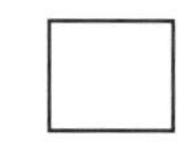 

a b c d e

1.  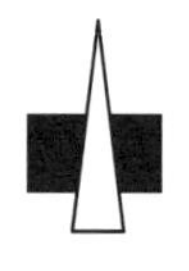  

a b c d e

2.   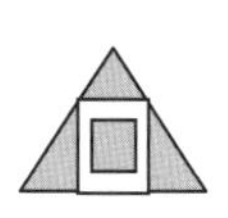   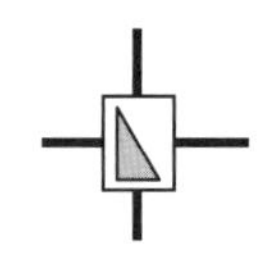

a b c d e

3.   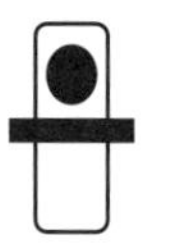  

a b c d e

4. 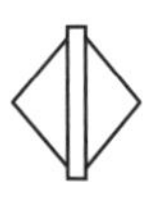 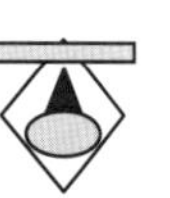 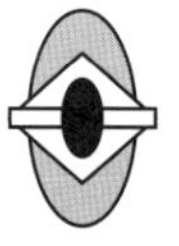  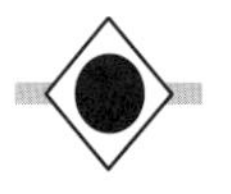 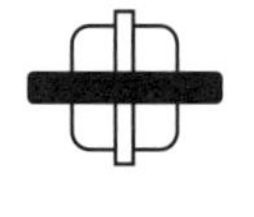

a b c d e

5.  

a b c d e

6.  

a b c d e

Now go on to the next page ➔

Pretend the dotted line is a mirror. Which picture on the right is a reflection of the picture on the left? Circle the letter.

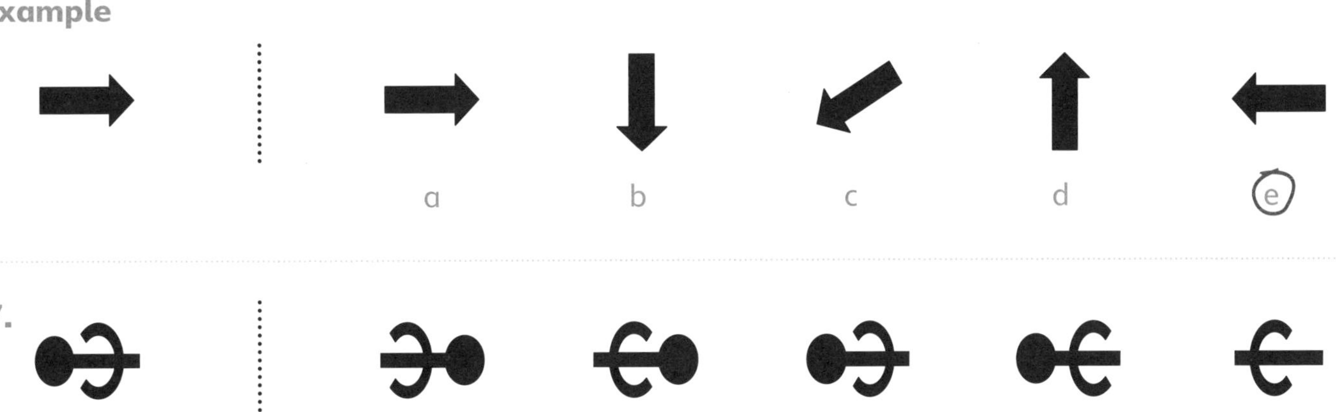

a b c d e

a b c d e

8.

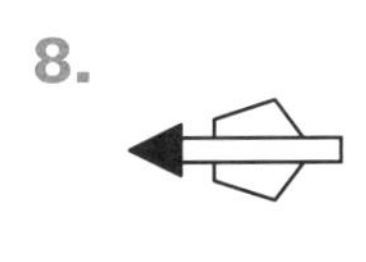 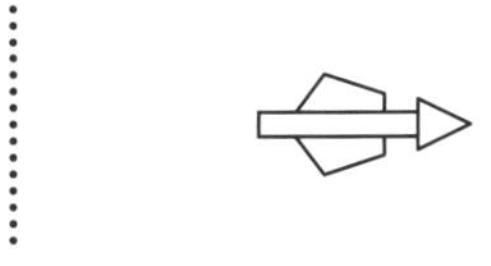   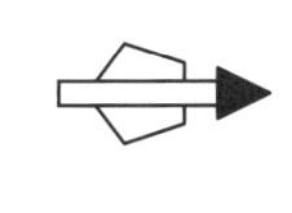 

a b c d e

9.

a b c d e

10.

 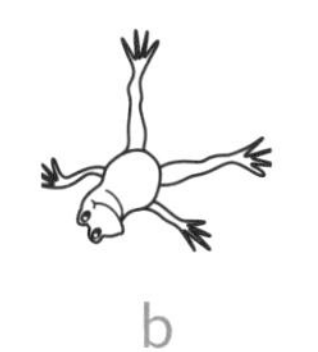   

a b c d e

11.

   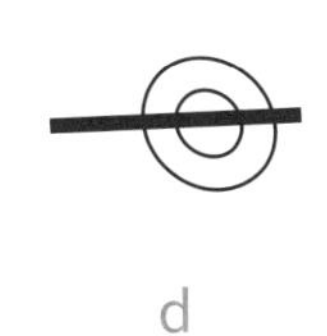 

a b c d e

12.

  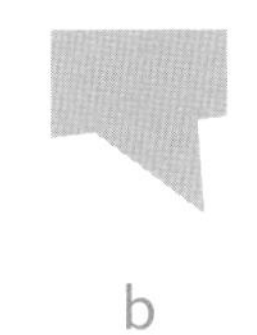   

a b c d e

End of test

Score:		Time taken:		Target met?	

Section 3 Test 4

Target time: **6 minutes**

Which of the pictures on the right best fits into the space in the grid? Circle the letter.

Example

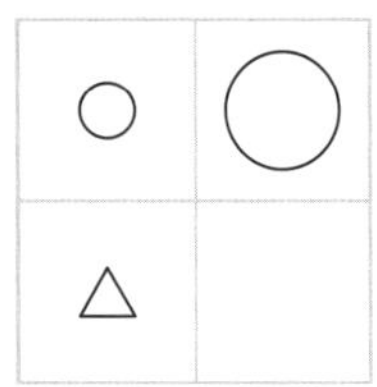

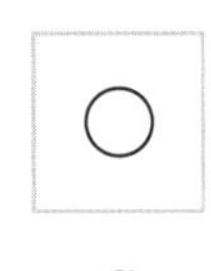 a

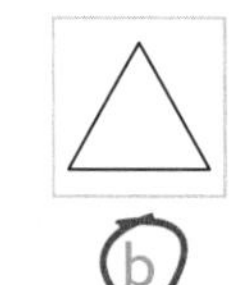 b

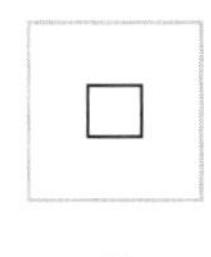 c

 d

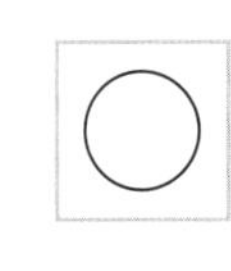 e

1.

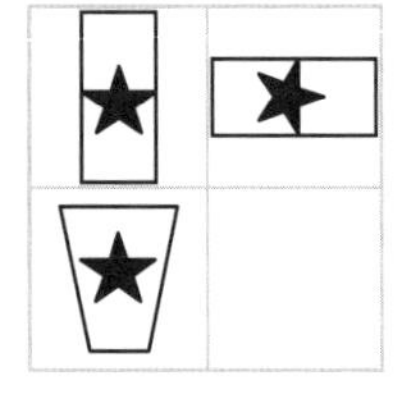

 a

 b

 c

 d

 e

2.

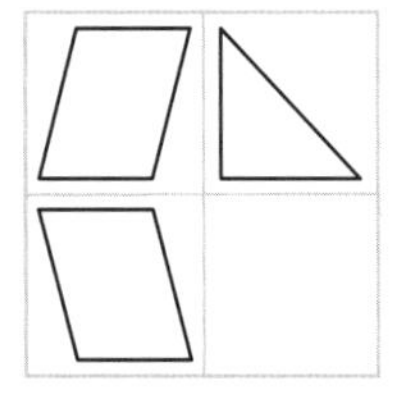

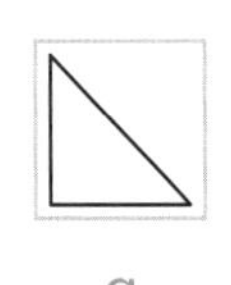 a

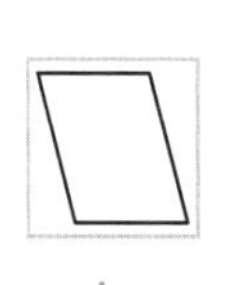 b

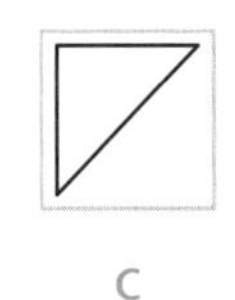 c

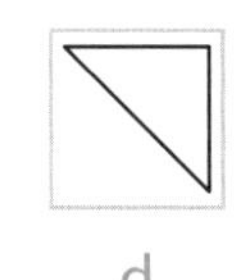 d

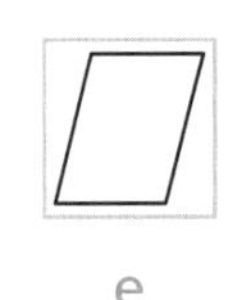 e

3.

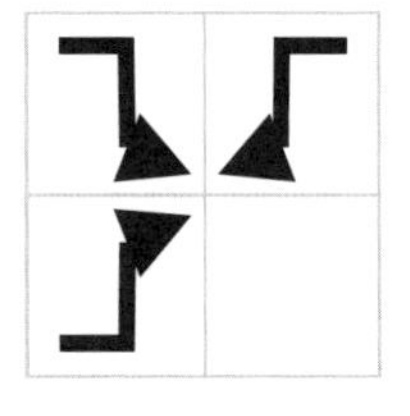

 a

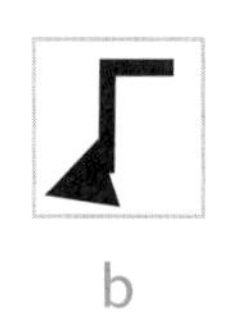 b

 c

 d

 e

4.

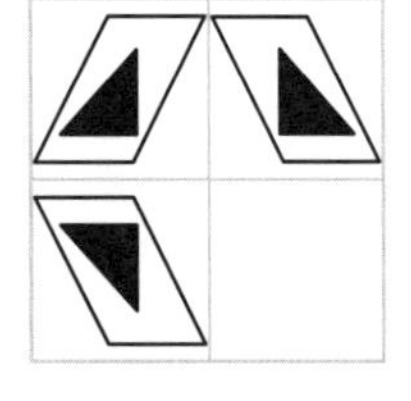

 a

 b

 c

 d

 e

5.

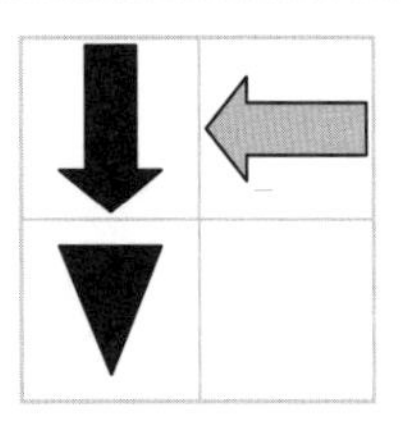

 a

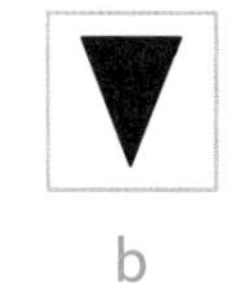 b

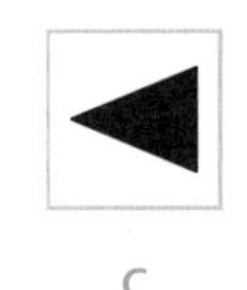 c

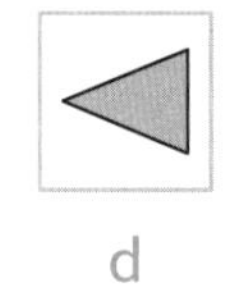 d

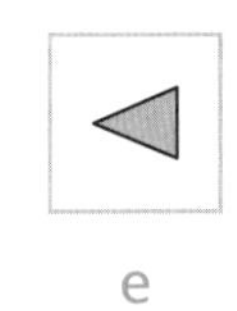 e

6.

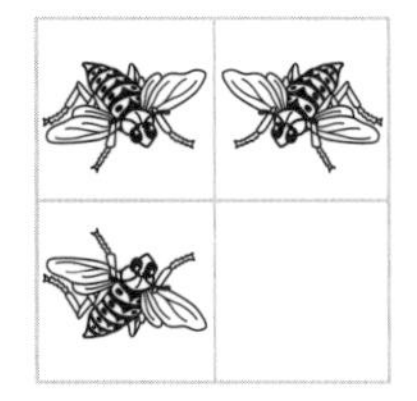

 a

 b

 c

 d

 e

Now go on to the next page ➔

Which picture on the right belongs to the group on the left? Circle the letter.

Example

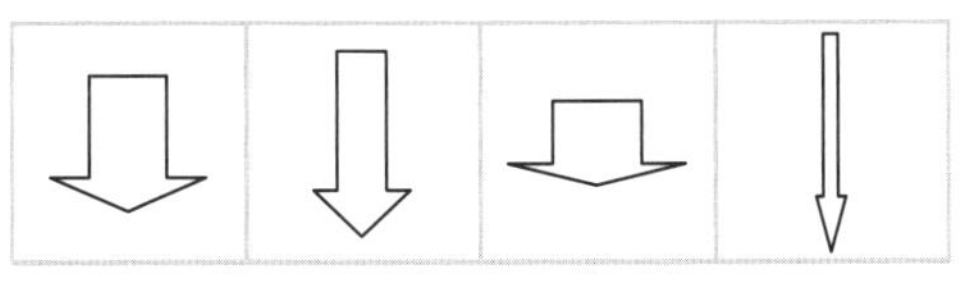

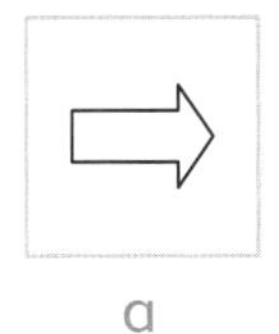 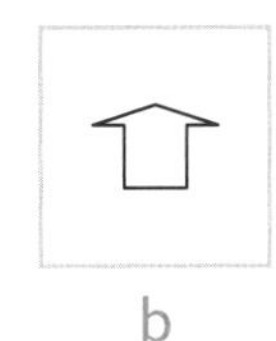 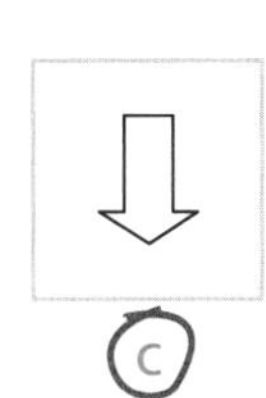 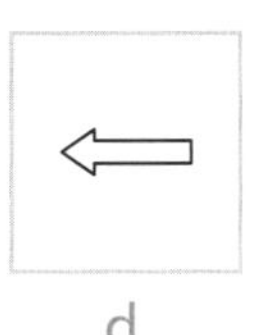 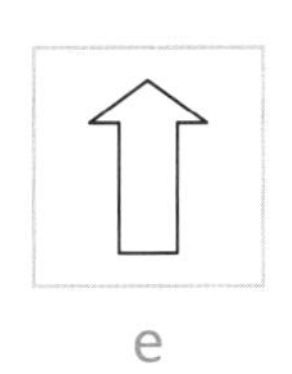

a b (c) d e

7. 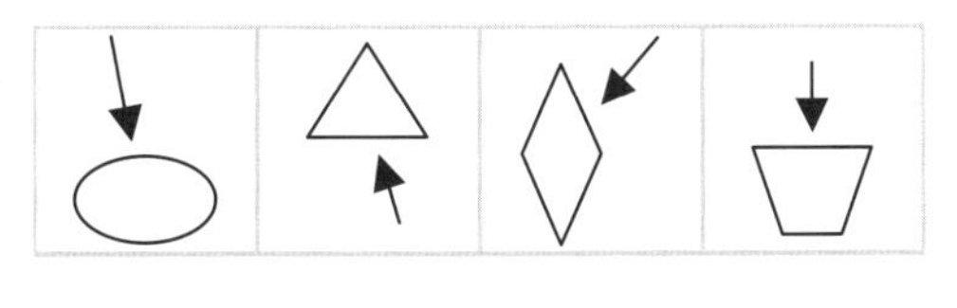

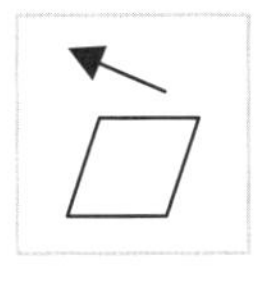 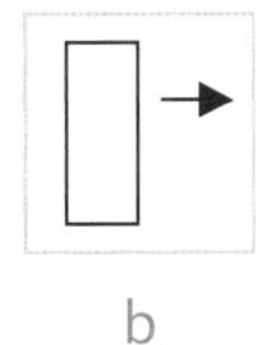 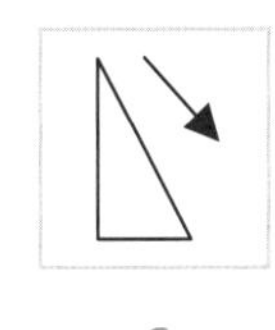  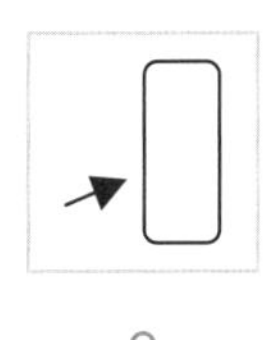

a b c d e

8. 

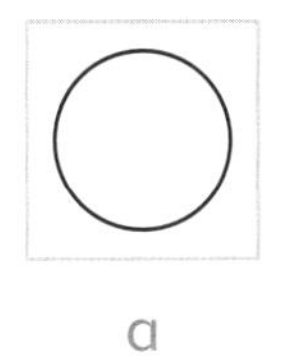 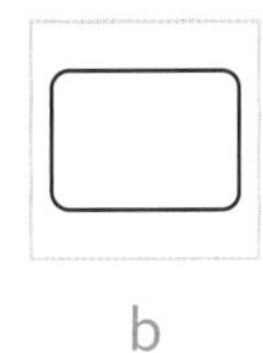  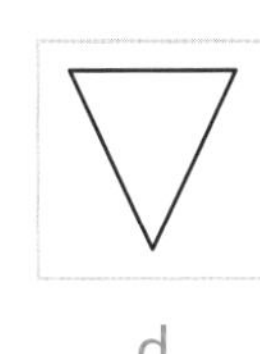 

a b c d e

9. 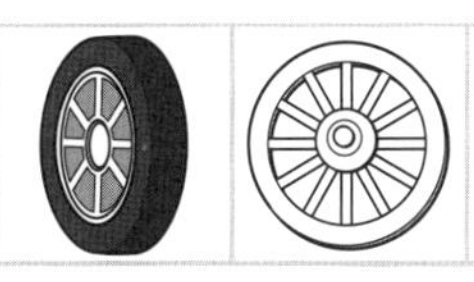 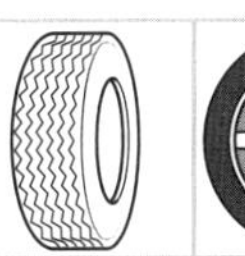 

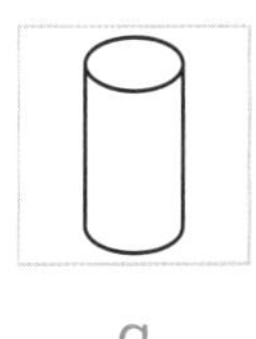   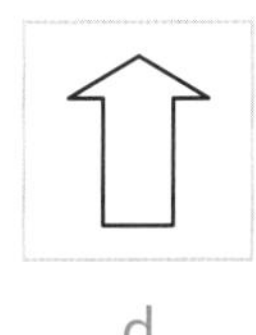 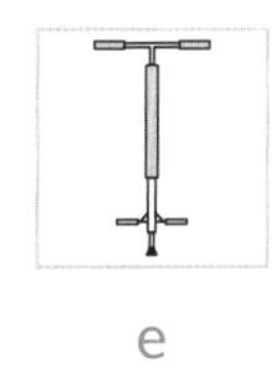

a b c d e

10. 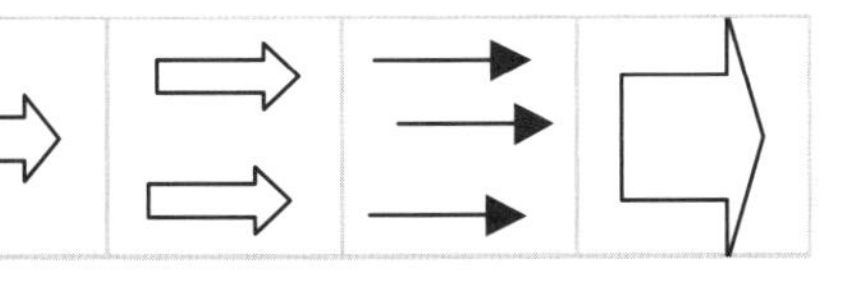

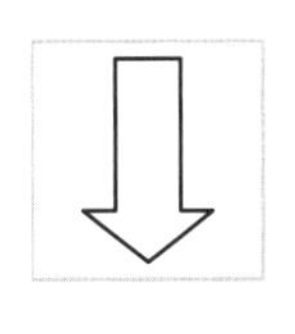 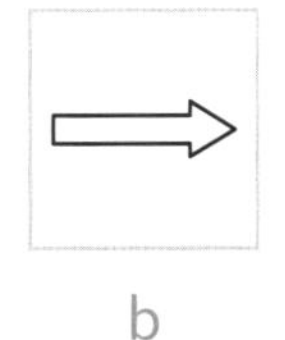  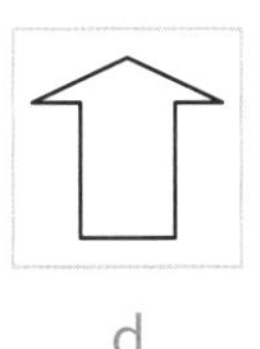 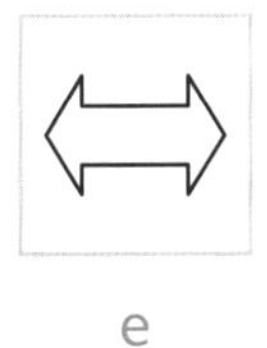

a b c d e

11. 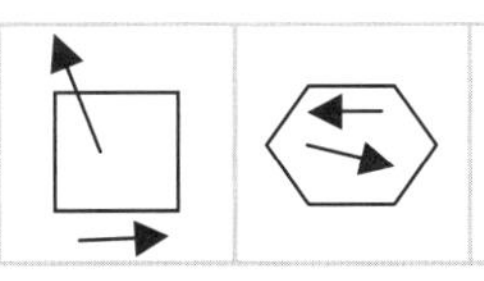 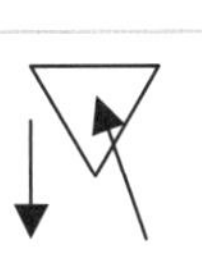 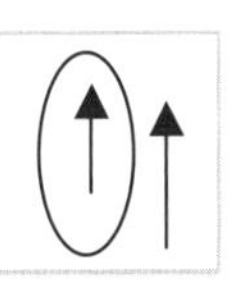

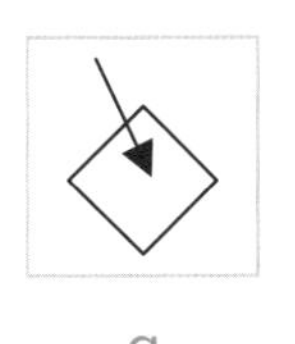 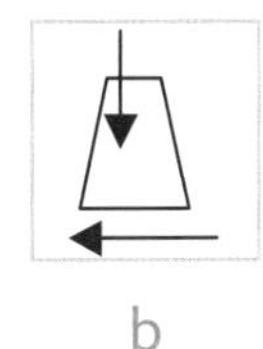 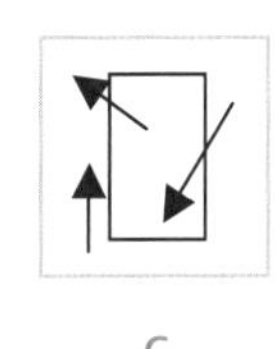 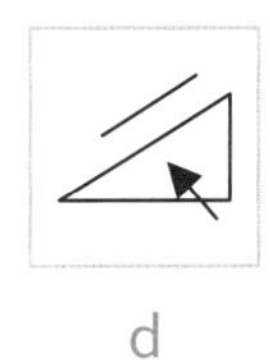 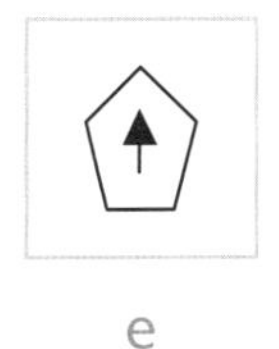

a b c d e

12. 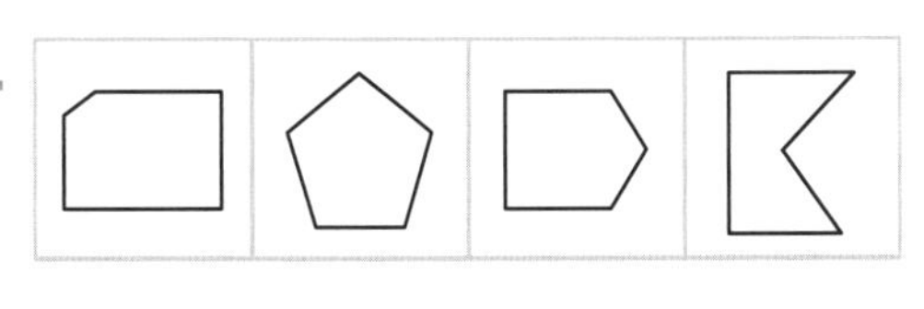

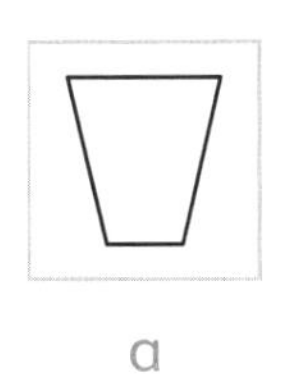 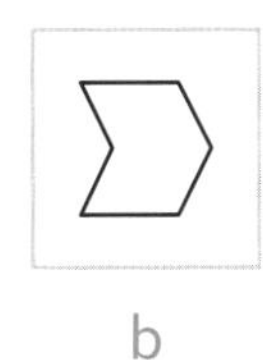 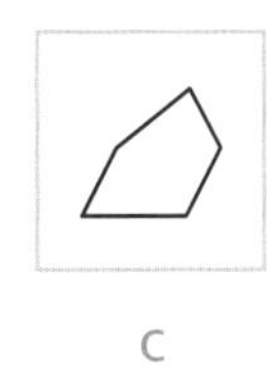 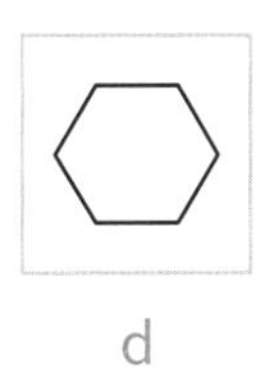 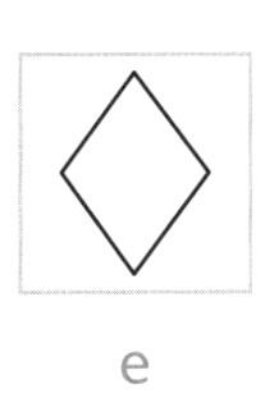

a b c d e

End of test

Score:		**Time taken:**		**Target met?**	

Target time: **6 minutes**

Which picture is the odd one out? Circle the letter.

Example

				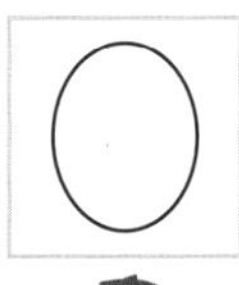
a	b	c	d	e

1.

	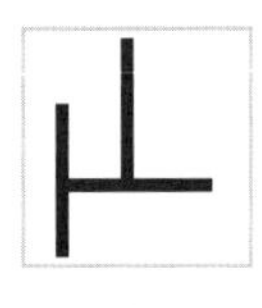	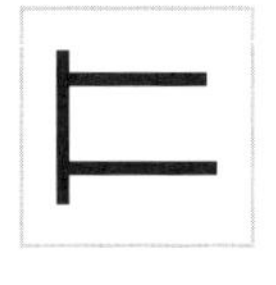	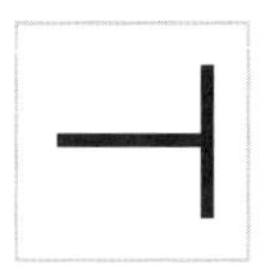	
a	b	c	d	e

2.

a	b	c	d	e

3.

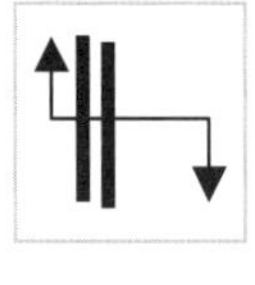	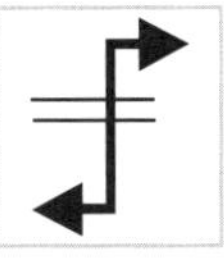		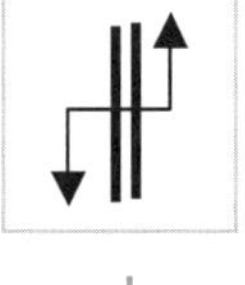	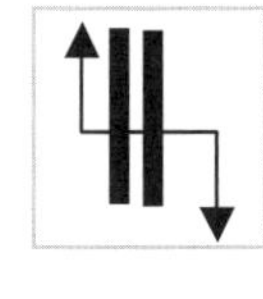
a	b	c	d	e

4.

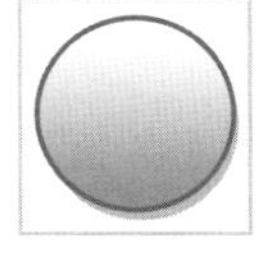				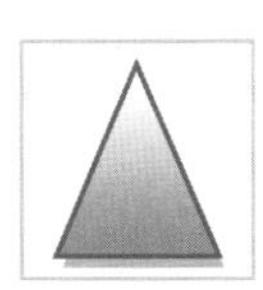
a	b	c	d	e

5.

a	b	c	d	e

6.

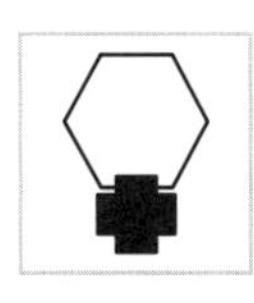	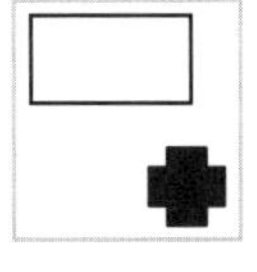	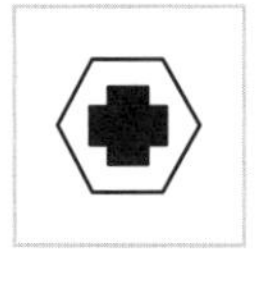	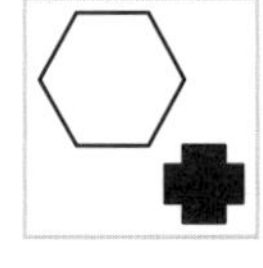	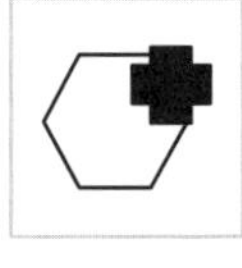
a	b	c	d	e

Now go on to the next page ➔

The first two pictures go together. Which of the five pictures on the right goes with the third picture in the same way? Circle the letter.

Example

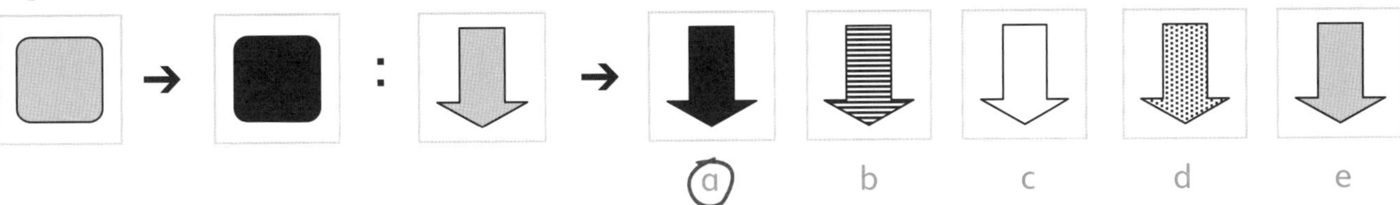

a b c d e

7.

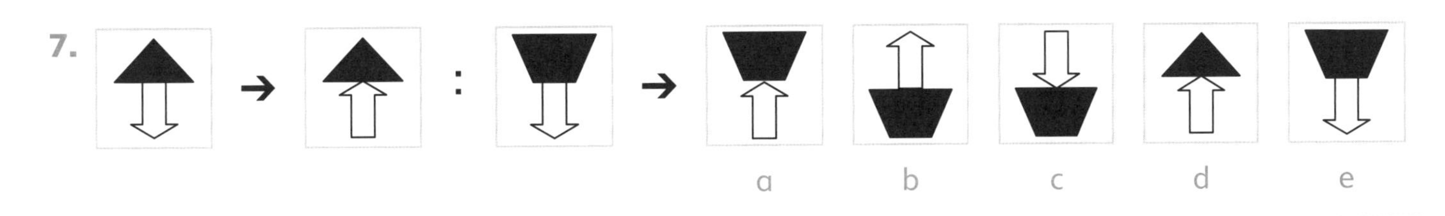

a b c d e

8.

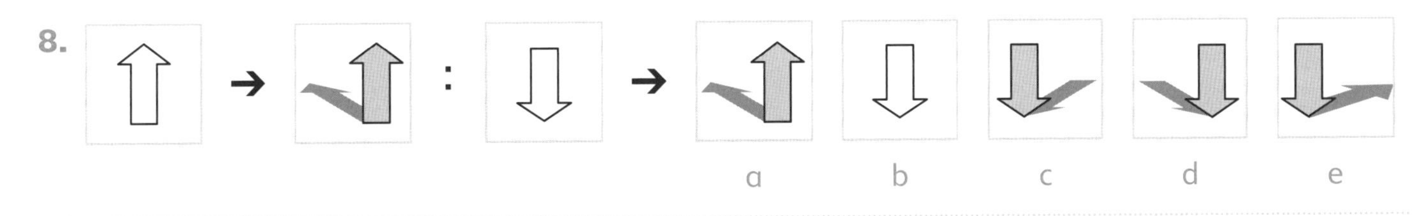

a b c d e

9.

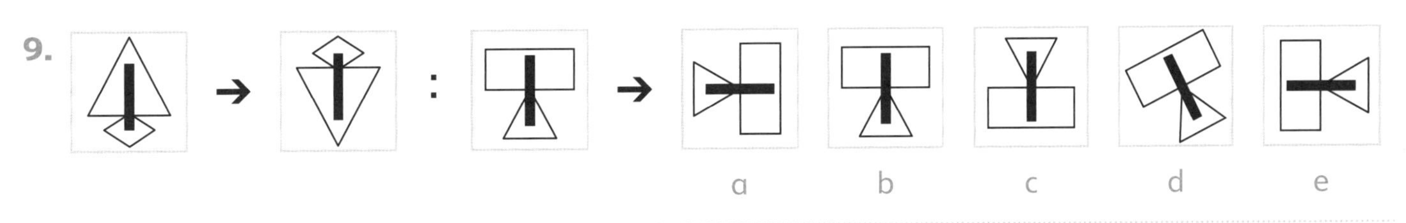

a b c d e

10.

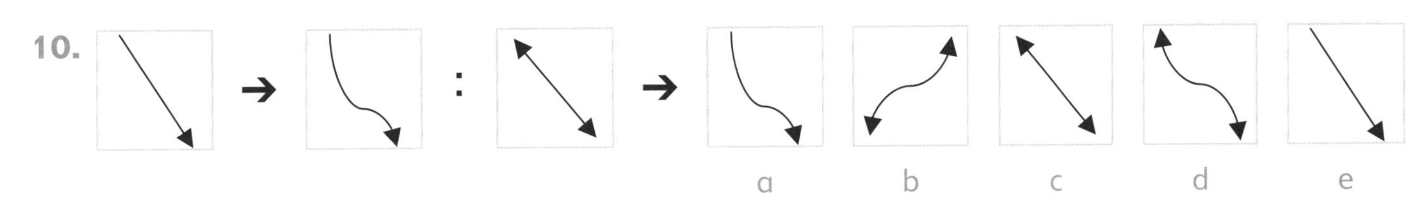

a b c d e

11.

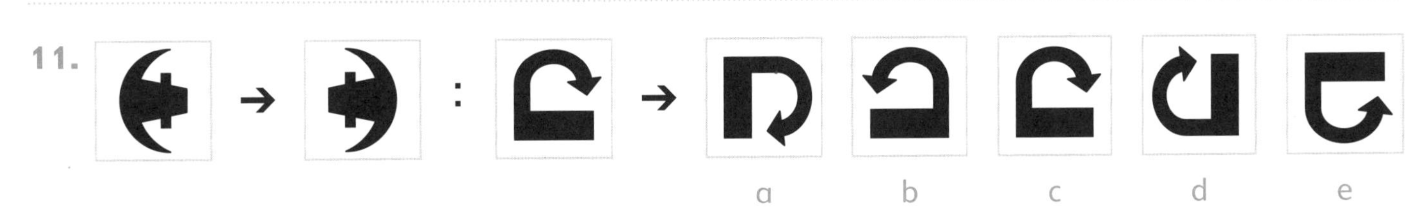

a b c d e

12.

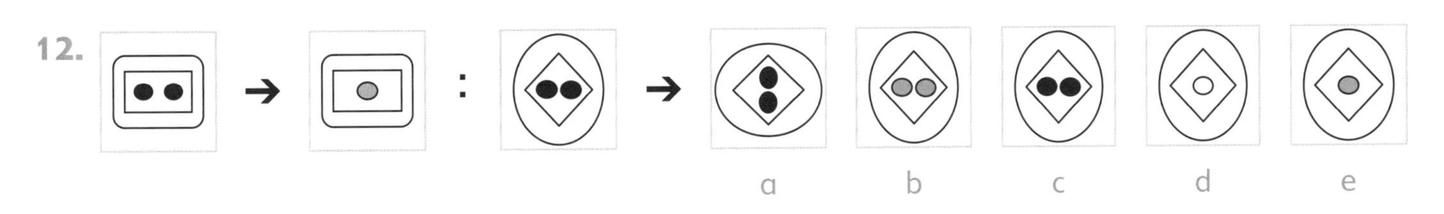

a b c d e

End of test

Score:		Time taken:		Target met?	

Target time: **6 minutes**

Which picture on the right goes in the empty space? Circle the letter.

Example

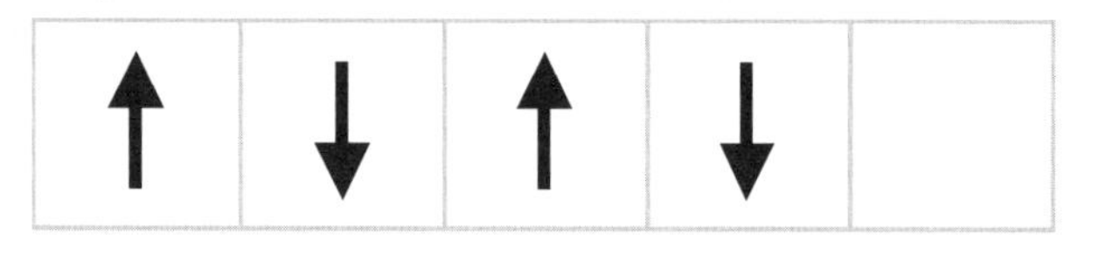

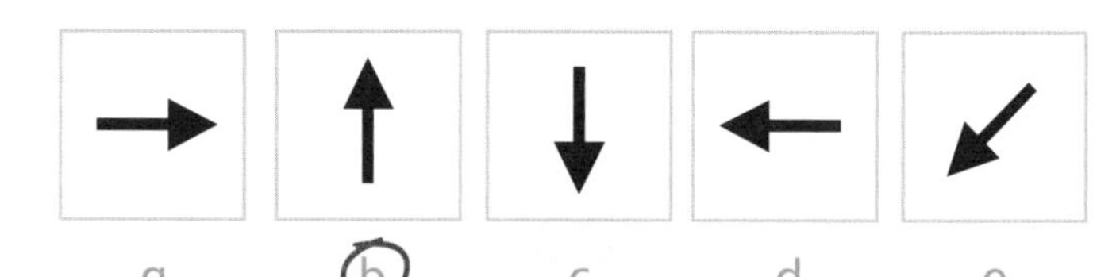

a (b) c d e

1.

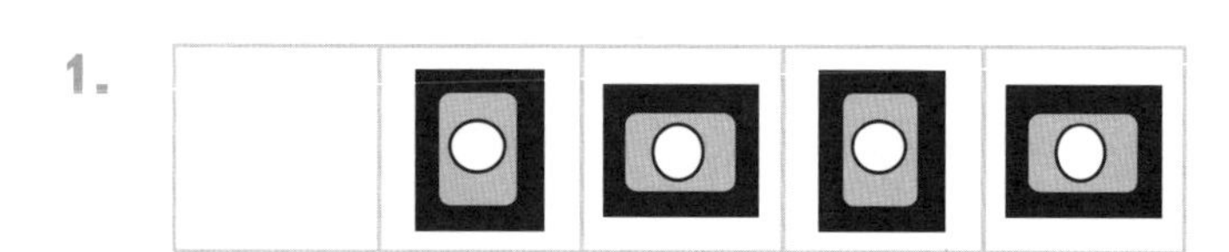

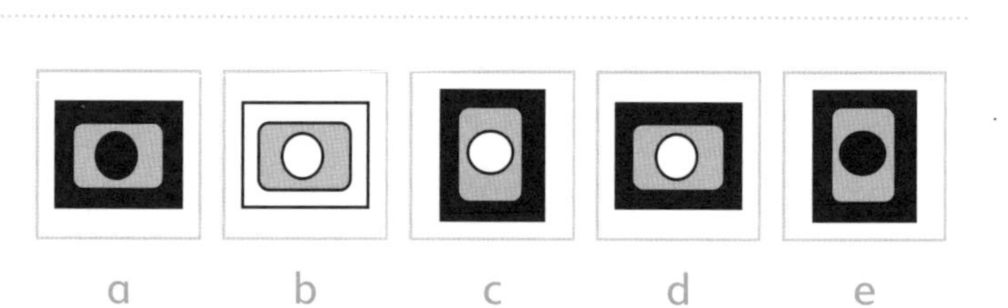

a b c d e

2.

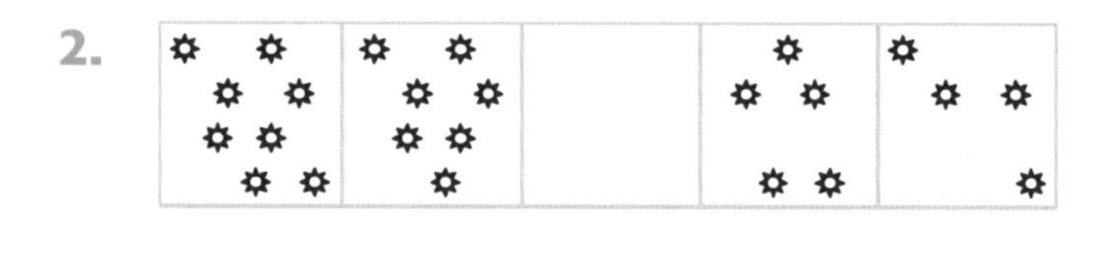

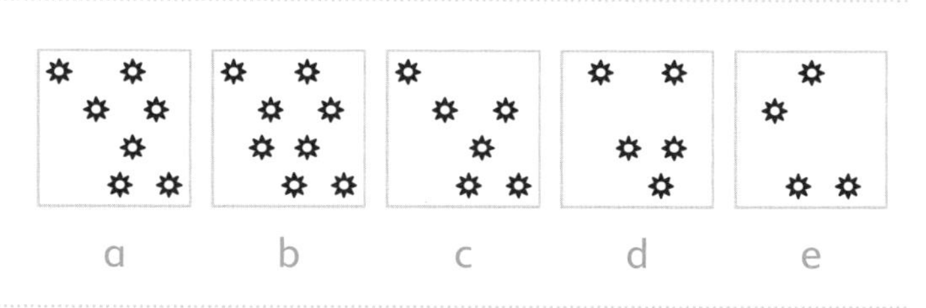

a b c d e

3.

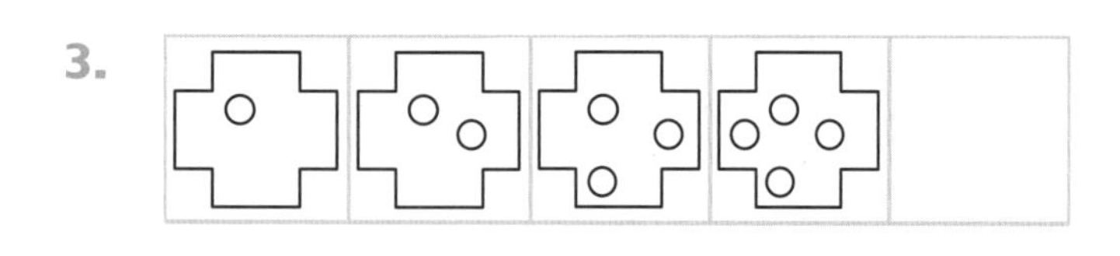

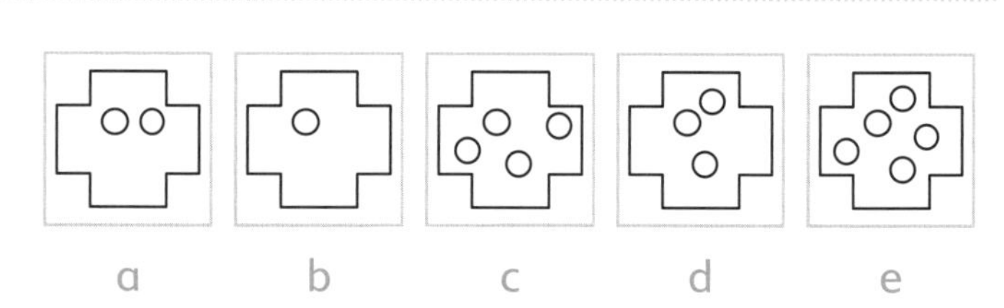

a b c d e

4.

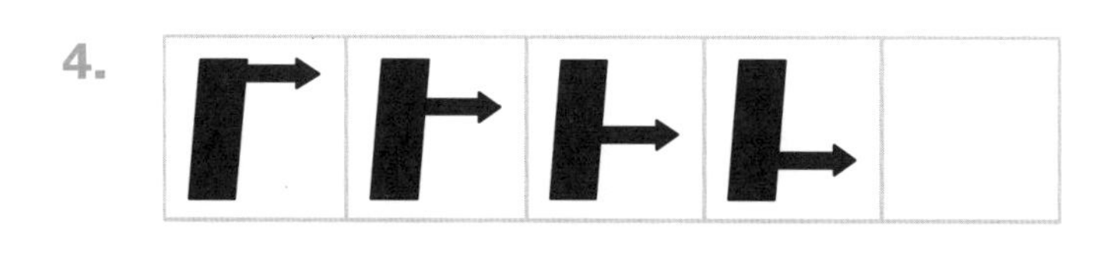

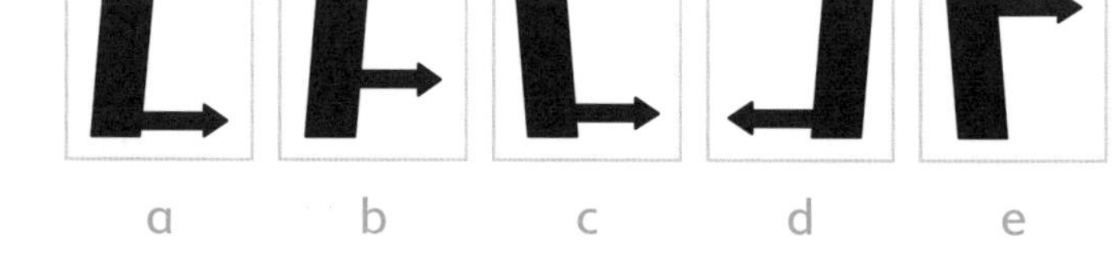

a b c d e

5.

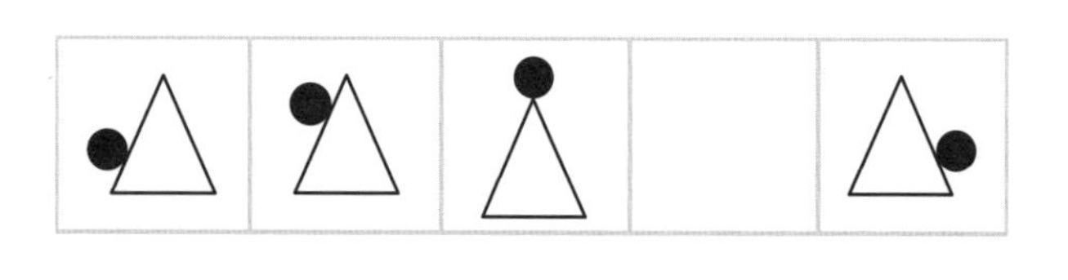

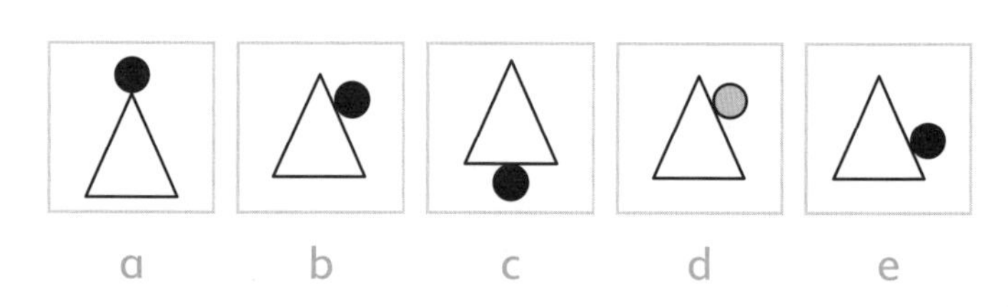

a b c d e

6.

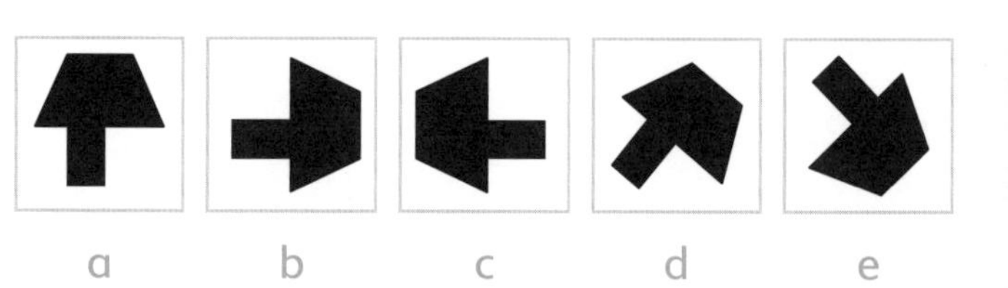

a b c d e

Now go on to the next page ➔

In which picture on the right is the picture on the left hidden? Circle the letter.

Example

a	b	c	d	e

7. 

a	b	c	d	e

8. 

a	b	c	d	e
		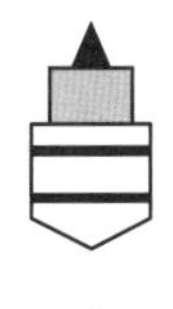		

9. 

a	b	c	d	e

10. 

a	b	c	d	e

11. 

a	b	c	d	e
			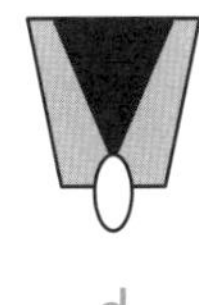	

12. 

a	b	c	d	e
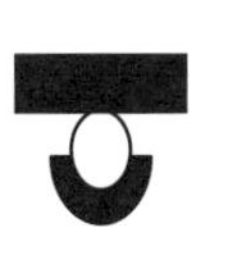				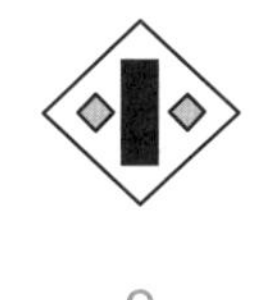

End of test

Score:		**Time taken:**		**Target met?**	

Progress chart

Write the score (out of 12) for each test in the box provided on the right of the graph. Then colour in the row next to the box to represent this score.

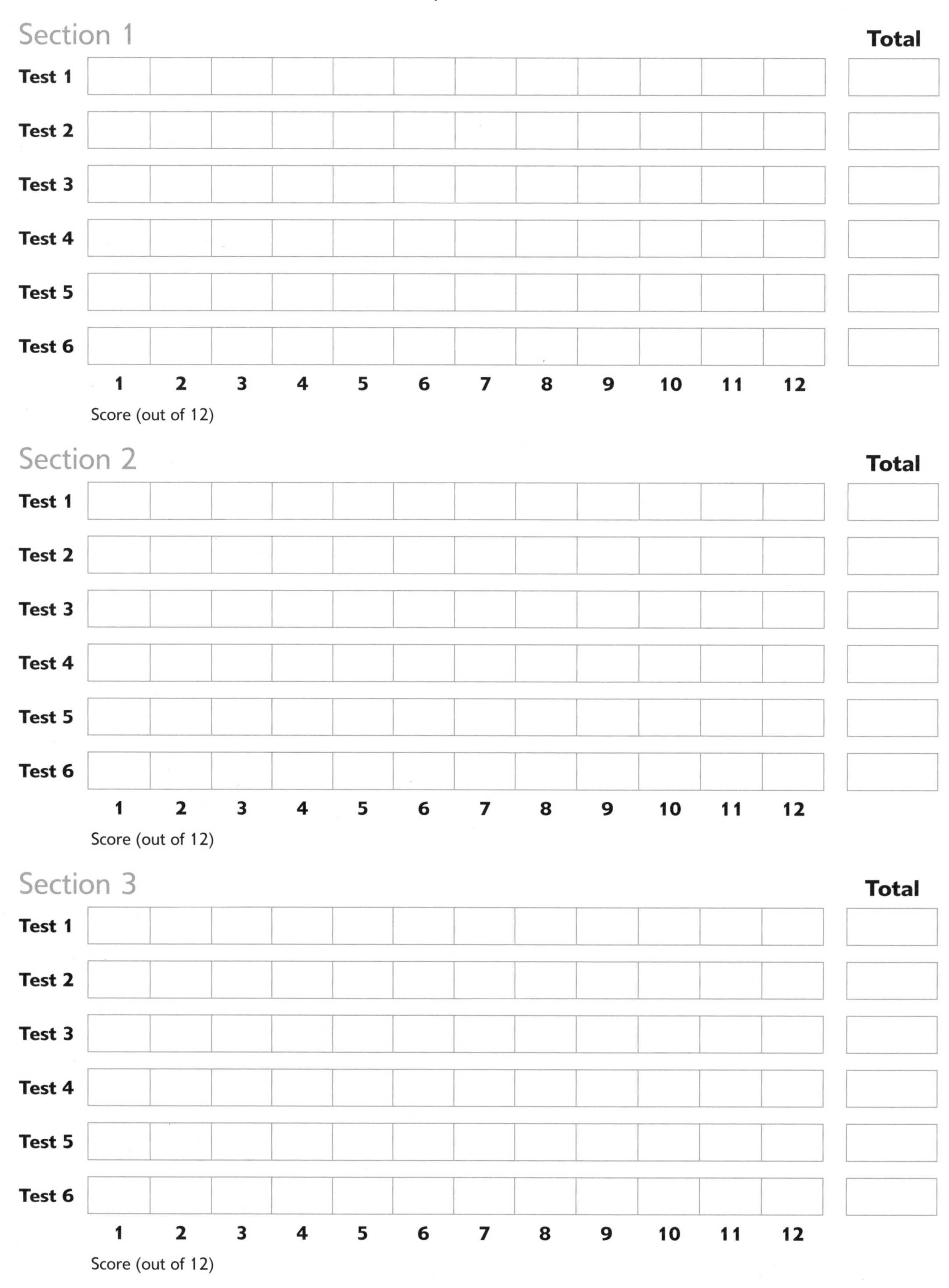